THE NEW ORLEANS VATICAN PAVILION LOGO

GIOTTO, THE ANGEL

TREASURES OF THE VATICAN

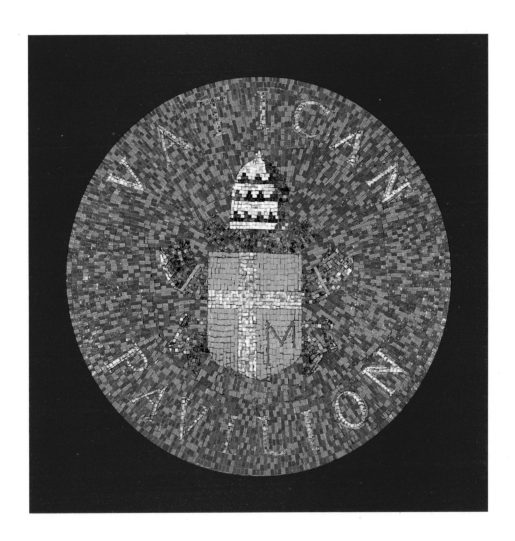

NEW ORLEANS VATICAN PAVILION AT THE 1984 LOUISIANA WORLD EXPOSITION

JESUS CHRIST OUR REDEEMER IN ART: AGES, IMAGES, IMPACT

THIS IS THE OFFICIAL NEW ORLEANS VATICAN PAVILION
CATALOGUE AUTHORIZED BY THE ARCHDIOCESE OF NEW ORLEANS
THE VERY REVEREND VAL A. McINNES, O.P. EDITOR

THE NEW ORLEANS VATICAN PAVILION,
PUBLISHERS

ACKNOWLEDGEMENTS

This exhibition is in collaboration with:

The New Orleans Museum of Art

The Vatican Museums
Apostolic Vatican Library
Sacristy, Sistine Chapel
Reverenda Fabbrica of St. Peter's

Musée du Louvre
Notre Dame de Paris
Musée de Cluny
Patrimoine de France
Musée Carnavalet
Romans, Église Collegiale St. Bernard
Musée Historique Orléans
Chapelle du Rosaire, Vence

La Santa Iglesia Catedral Primada
Toledo

The Philadelphia Museum of Art

The Henry Moore Foundation

The National Gallery of Ireland

The National Gallery of Canada
Musée du Québec

The National Map Collection, Public Archives,
Canada
The Macdonald-Stewart Foundation
Notre Dame de Montréal

The Snite Museum

Marquette University Art Museum

The Ringling Museum

African Art Museum of the Society of African
Missions

Private Collections

The New Orleans Vatican Pavilion wishes to acknowledge the contribution of McDermott Incorporated which made this publication possible.

The installation of the works of art has been made possible in part by a generous grant from The Koch Foundation.

Pan-American World Airways, Incorporated, which has been the carrier for the Vatican Exhibition in the United States, has graciously agreed to continue the same service for the New Orleans Vatican Pavilion as our official international carrier.

Delta Airlines has been named the official domestic carrier.

Air Canada, and Aer Lingus, have been named our official carriers of their nations' respective works of art.

The Sheraton New Orleans has been named the official hotel for the New Orleans Vatican Pavilion.

We acknowledge with gratitude the services of Stewart Enterprises, Incorporated.

We thank Mr. Frank Kacmarcik for the design of the Church and Water Logo, Mr. William V. Cladek for the Fountain and Altar design, and Dr. Virginia Koch for the musical selections especially arranged for the Vatican Pavilion Exhibition.

Special storage services courtesy of David Oreck and The Security Center of New Orleans.

American Rent All, Incorporated, has graciously provided invaluable services in regard to the installation of the works of art.

CONTENTS

Joannes Paulus PP. II

HIS HOLINESS POPE JOHN PAUL II

SECRETARIAT OF STATE

No. 115.630   FROM THE VATICAN, August 27, 1983

Dear Archbishop Hannan,

　　His Holiness Pope John Paul II was happy
to be informed of the preparations being made
for the Vatican Pavilion at the 1984 Louisiana
World Exposition in New Orleans. He extends
a warm greeting to all those who will visit this
Pavilion, praying that they will be uplifted
in spirit and renewed in faith by the works of
sacred art presented for their admiration.

　　The Holy Father is especially pleased that
these artistic pieces were chosen not only because
they reflect the glory of God and the beauty
of his creation, but even more because they point
to the mystery of the Redemption in our Lord
Jesus Christ, which is the pivotal event of all
human history. His Holiness prays that just
as the death and Resurrection of Christ, the
Incarnate Word of God, is commemorated and relived
in the Church by believers of every age, so this
exhibition of religious art will bear witness
to this great mystery and will help all those
who see it to penetrate its depth of meaning.

　　His Holiness invokes upon all visitors to
this Pavilion God's blessings of joy and peace.

　　　　　　　　　　　　Sincerely yours in Christ,

　　　　　　　　　　　　Secretary of State

The Most Reverend Philip M. Hannan
Archbishop of New Orleans

Most Reverend Philip M. Hannan, D.D., J.C.D.
Archbishop of New Orleans
President

Very Reverend Val A. McInnes, O.P., Ph.D.
Director

John F. Screen
General Manager

614 Tchoupitoulas Street
(504) 525-6166

Message of Welcome from Archbishop Hannan,

Official Host of the New Orleans Vatican Pavilion,

Louisiana World Exposition, 1984.

It is with great joy that we greet all the people visiting this Vatican Pavilion under the theme, "Redemption of Mankind". The Redemption of Mankind involves all the activities of men and women, especially in art, through the ages as well as in its images and impact which have effected evangelization in the world today. Since the Church has been and continues to support all that is good in the human condition, these works of art on loan from the Vatican Collections distill in an artistic way the vital mysteries of our faith and the humanity of Christ Himself.

We note, therefore, with pleasure that the overall theme for the Louisiana Exposition is <u>Rivers and Waters - the Sources of our Lives</u>. We heartily endorse this theme since Jesus Himself revealed to the Samaritan woman at the incident of Jacob's well "...anyone who drinks the water that I shall give will never be thirsty again: the water that I shall give will turn into a spring inside of him, welling up to eternal life." (John 4:13-14)

These art treasures speak to us of renewing the well springs of our faith. Through the creativity and genius of the individual artists we catch a new and refreshing glance into the mysteries of the faith. Recently, the Holy Father said that through the works of art in the Vatican, "the Church continues to carry out one of its fundamental tasks, that of evangelization." He stated that viewing these works of art "can also represent the first occasion for a happy and significant encounter with the Christian message and that the Church is not indifferent to or estranged from anything that is human." We are deeply indebted to the Holy Father for granting permission for the loan of these works of art. The generosity of His Holiness, Pope John Paul 11, gives us the opportunity of sharing some of the significant Judeo-Christian treasures with many people who would not otherwise have the opportunity of seeing them first hand in Rome.

"Evangelization in the World Today"

Moreover, we decided to invite the founding nations of Louisiana, France and Spain who have agreed to loan a few of their own religious masterpieces to the Vatican Pavilion as well. Those nations were most instrumental in bringing the faith to the new world. Also that same faith was developed through the peoples from Italy, England, Africa, Ireland and Canada. It is, therefore, very appropriate that they too have agreed to loan some significant works of art representing their cultural tradition and religious gifts to Louisiana. How fortunate for the Vatican Pavilion to have these works of art included.

May all who visit the Vatican Pavilion realize the full message expressed in these works of art as stated by the Holy Father, "Man cannot live without love. He remains a being that is incomprehensible for himself, his life is senseless, if love is not revealed to him, if he does not encounter love, if he does not experience it and make it his own, if he does not participate intimately in it. This, as has already been said, is why Christ the Redeemer 'fully reveals man to himself'."

Philip M. Hannan

+Philip M. Hannan
Archbishop of New Orleans

ARCHBISHOP PHILIP M. HANNAN

TREASURES OF THE VATICAN

T HROUGHOUT THE Christian era, artists have devoted their talents to the life, death, and resurrection of Christ. In their works of art, they have attempted to portray the great and startling fact that God became man in Jesus Christ.

Men have often claimed to be godlike, but only once in all history has God claimed to be man. For this reason, the life and mission of Jesus Christ captivate and inspire. Believer and unbeliever alike have been moved thereby to attempt the impossible, to capture in artistic works the transcendence they perceive in Christ. The life of Christ, ever so fascinating, continues in our own day to stimulate and enrich the imagination and creative genius of men and women of great artistic talent.

The New Orleans Vatican Pavilion Exhibition is entitled: Jesus Christ Our Redeemer in Art: Ages, Images, and Impact.

The Exhibition unfolds before us a spectrum of religious art, in the context of today's evangelization.

Pagan, Jewish, and Christian memorial glasses bear witness to an early belief in immortality. Artistic images attest to that same hope for immortality. In this area alone, pagan, Jewish and Christian artists, in creating beautiful works, somehow testify to one's unvoiced "intimations of immortality."

In every age, faith finds expression in works of art. Each age has its own peculiar style. During the ages of faith, the Primitive Period was succeeded by the Romanesque and Byzantine, Carolingian and Gothic. These were followed by the Renaissance and the Baroque, which in time yielded to the Romantic and Modern periods. We are witnessing a renewed expression of Christian art in a contemporary mode. Christianity has left its hallmark on the ingenuity and creative imagination of the ages. The living flame of Christ, who is the "Light of the World" and the "Source of Living Water," has captured the imagination of artists. Turning their creative genius to the mysteries of the faith, they have produced a "living art" which reaches out to us, touching and transforming hearts and helping to make us a new people. Not all religious art is of the highest caliber, of course, but occasional "living" masterpieces more than make up for that, and remain as a living witness to the artist's profound faith and genius.

The images which have come down to us in all their beauty are also a kind of case history that reflect the historical milieu into which they first came, and bear witness to the peculiar way artistic inspiration struck a rich chord in the heart of the artist. Works of significant aesthetic value provide us with a kaleidoscope of the profound mysteries of the faith. From time immemorial, beginning with the first pages of the Bible, artists have encountered that new creation which is Christ and his Church. Their artistic reactions to that fact have given us works that delight, entertain, provoke, and challenge the viewer.

The impact of great works of art is incalculable. Each is a kind of prism through which we glimpse something of the religious faith, politics, and artistry of the era which witnessed their birth.

The Vatican Pavilion makes accessible to the public a cross-section of some of the choicest pieces in the Vatican Collections. Their loan was made possible by Pope John Paul II, who graciously gave his all-important permission. His Eminence Cardinal Casaroli was also generously supportive of the idea. We thank Archbishop Paul Marcinkus for his intervention on our behalf. Without these three men, this Exposition would not have been possible.

We wish also to thank the Director General of the Vatican Museums, Professor Carlo Pietrangeli, and Dr. Walter Persegati, Secretary and Treasurer of the Vatican Museums, who helped us choose these representative works. We are also sincerely grateful to Archbishop Peter Van Lierde, Vicar General of Vatican City, Archbishop Lino Zanini, Delegate of the Fabbrica of St. Peter's, to Archbishop Alfons Stickler, Prefect of the Apostolic Vatican Library, and to Mrs. Patricia Bonicatti for their diligent and helpful assistance.

To Marcelo Cardinal Gonzalez of Toledo we owe our profound thanks; indeed we express the same gratitude to Jean-Marie Cardinal Lustiger of Paris, and to President Mitterrand and Mr. Jack Lang, Minister of Culture for France, for their generous response; Mr. Jack Meurisse of the Patrimoine de France, and M. Michel Laclotte, Inspector General of the Museums of France, were most helpful. Mr. Pierre Rosenburg, Director of Paintings, Musée du Louvre, was very kind and generous. The same is true of the invaluable assistance of Mesdames Regine Pernoud and Marie Véronique Clin-Meyer of the Centre Jeanne d'Arc of Orléans. Thanks are due to the Director of the Musée de Cluny, Mr. Alain Erlande-Brandenburg, and to Mr. Jacques Blanc, our adviser and close friend in Paris. The Direc-

JESUS CHRIST OUR REDEEMER IN ART: AGES, IMAGES AND IMPACT

tor of the National Gallery of Ireland, Mr. Honan Potterton, and his associate, Mr. Raymond Keaveney were equally generous and responsive to our requests. Mr. Henry Moore and The Henry Moore Foundation were most kind with their loan as well.

On our own continent, the Secretary of State for Canada, the Honorable Mr. Serge Joyal, and the National Gallery of Canada responded to our requests with considerate and generous permissions. Mr. Joseph Martin, the Director of the National Gallery, and his associates were most kind. The *Musée du Québec* and its Director, Mr. Pierre Lachapelle, and Mr. André Kaltenback reconfirmed the bonds of friendship with Louisiana by giving their total cooperation. Without the generous support of the following institutions we could not have produced such a significant exhibition: Marquette University Fine Arts Committee, The Snite Museum of the University of Notre Dame, The Ringling Museum, The African Museum of the Society of African Missions, The National Map Collection, Public Archives, Canada, and the Macdonald-Stewart Foundation for the use of their significant maps and the coordination of the loan of the Canadian works of art.

Closer to home, we wish to acknowledge the help of the Staff and Members of the New Orleans Museum of Art, one of our outstanding American museums. Special mention should be made of Mr. E. John Bullard, Director of the Museum; he and his Staff and Members of the Museum are co-sponsors of the Vatican Exposition, thereby assuring to it the professional expertise which will enhance its presentation. For their contribution, we are both grateful and deeply indebted.

Special thanks are hereby tendered to Mr. Stuart Silver and his associate, Mr. Clifford LaFontaine, for good advice on many matters and for the design of the interiors and the exhibitions; also to our able architects, Messrs. Blitch and Associates, our contractor, Gervais F. Favrot Company, Inc., our loyal and diligent General Manager, Mr. John F. Screen, and the Staff of the New Orleans Vatican Pavilion.

Our New Orleans Vatican Pavilion Board, which has overseen the building for our exhibition, has worked effectively and successfully to satisfy the rigorous requirements laid down by the design program and the museum requirements. Thanks are due to our Chairman, Mr. Alden J. Laborde, and Msgr. Charles Duke.

It was His Excellency, Archbishop Philip M. Hannan of New Orleans, who extended to France and Spain an invitation to contribute some of their major pieces of religious art to the Vatican Exposition, especially as these countries played so great a part in the formation of Louisiana. Nor were they the only ones; New Orleans grew through waves of immigration which brought to our shores peoples from Italy, England, Ireland, and Canada. Their respective countries were accordingly invited to participate. Their response was gratifying, and the Vatican Exhibition now also contains some excellent pieces from these countries. And from the African peoples too: Nigeria and Ethiopia have contributed works of art which reflect the rich, black, Christian cultural heritage of their lands.

To all these nations and various institutions, then, our profound thanks. Their presence at the Vatican Exhibition will undoubtedly deepen the awareness of the people of Louisiana-and others as well-of how much we have been enriched by this variety of cultures.

Christ and his life are the inspiration of most of these works of art. It was he who inspired the artists to discover hitherto unexplored facets of the mystery of Christ. This variety of insights is precisely what is meant by the gospel-word: like the faithful steward, the artist is a prophet and teacher who knows how to bring forth "things both new and old" (Matthew 13:52).

The success of this Vatican Exposition will in the end be determined by you, the viewer. We hope you will, like so many generations that have gone before you, derive much pleasure and enjoyment from these works. May they renew the wellspring of your faith and hope in the Lord. And may he continue to make all things new through his artists, and those of you who contemplate and admire their work.

THE VERY REVEREND VAL A. McINNES, O.P.
DIRECTOR, NEW ORLEANS VATICAN PAVILION

LIVING WATERS

THE THEME for the Louisiana Exposition 1984 is *Rivers and Waters: The Sources of Our Lives.* This refreshing theme brings to mind images of fountains, wells, waterfalls, lakes and streams, all fusing together as they cascade down from the mountains into the rivers which then make their way to the sea. The mighty Mississippi gathers waters from the central mountains and plains from the East and West and drains down through the Mississippi Valley past New Orleans and on to the vast expanse of sea in the Gulf of Mexico. Water is a fitting theme for Louisiana and the city of New Orleans. Most of our state exists because of its abundant waterways which have made commerce possible. Cotton, rice and sugar cane, watered by abundant rains, are commodities for which Louisiana is famous.

The theme of the New Orleans Vatican Pavilion fits into the theme of the Louisiana World Exposition in an unusual way. The explicit theme is *Jesus Christ Our Redeemer in Art: Ages, Images and Impact on Evangelization in the World Today.* The related theme we have chosen to tie into the overall theme of the Fair is *Jesus Christ, The Source of Living Waters.* As one reflects upon the themes of art, religion, and water in the context of redemption and evangelization, several sudden and unexpected strands of unity appear.

First of all, from the earliest times water has been at the center of the mystery of redemption. At creation, the Spirit hovered over primordial waters. Throughout the Bible water is synonymous with life. In the arid land where the Chosen People of God lived, one pursued life close to a river, a well, or an oasis; without these sources of water they would have perished.

When I visited Israel recently, the significance of water and the central place it plays in the lives of the People of God made a strong impression on me. With other pilgrims, I visited the ancient biblical site, Jacob's well. Here for centuries the People of God watered their flocks and refreshed themselves on its sweet, living waters. This well is a source of life in an otherwise arid and barren land.

On one occasion, Jesus sought refreshment at this very well after a long day's journey. He sent his disciples into town to acquire food; he remained behind at the well. While waiting for their return, he fell into conversation with a Samaritan woman. Even though she was, to many, a hated Samaritan, Jesus spoke to her and used the occasion to reveal in a sudden and unexpected way the mystery of his life and his mission.

The whole incident occurred simply, yet the full impact of his words has reverberated down the centuries. Jesus asked for a drink and went on to promise the woman living water. She observed that he did not have a bucket to draw water with, but he responded, "If you knew who it is who is speaking to you, you would ask of him and he would give you living water" (John 4:10). Her response to the invitation was uncomprehending and too literal.

This direct, uncomplicated dialogue illustrates the confluence of all that is human and divine in our lives. We might sum it up in the words, "the well and the church," an unusual phrase which brings us to the heart of our exhibition: evangelization, and the overall significance of waters and redemption.

On the site of Jacob's well, many churches have been constructed. The latest of these is an unfinished structure, left incomplete because of the unrest and troubled nature of the whole area. Over the centuries, the well has been carefully covered. Without a guide, you might easily pass it by. One descends a labyrinthian staircase to reach the opening to the well, which is quite deep. Its water, drawn up with a pail, is sweet and clear.

When Christ identified himself with the "living

waters," he was revealing in biblical terms the symbol of his divinity. Without "living waters" people cannot live; without Christ, the source of "everlasting living waters," the People of God cannot enter fully into the eternal friendship of the Kingdom of God.

The Judeo-Christian tradition of water reaches back to the dawn of creation. Genesis tells us how God created the heavens, the earth and the seas, and notes that the Spirit hovered over the waters. Later, the People of God were punished for their infidelity; all perished in the flood except Noah, his family, and the animals in the Ark. Later still, when God's People were exiled in Egypt, he raised up Moses whose name means "taken from waters" (Exodus 2:10). Moses, inspired by God, led the Jewish people through the waters of the Red Sea into the desert where some grumbled and complained against God for bringing them to such a desolate spot to die. But at God's command Moses struck the rock, and from it there came forth "living waters" to preserve the sons and daughters of God. After forty years of wandering in the wilderness, they passed through the waters of the River Jordan and entered into the long hoped-for Promised Land.

Once settled, they took up the life of shepherds and farmers. The land was harsh and survival was contingent on the all-important Jordan River and the rare and hard-to-find wells and cisterns. Jacob (Gen. 33:18) acquired the well which was to bear his name for centuries. Countless generations of livestock and families were to be nourished and preserved from this well-spring.

Through the whole of the Old Testament, and also in the New, stories of God's strong and life-giving presence run like a deep subterranean river. His wells are always full and ready to be drawn from, yet manifested only at intervals to reassure people that God's providence is a tangible reality—as tangible as "living waters."

Jesus' public ministry began with his baptism in the waters of the River Jordan. As John the Baptist poured the waters over Jesus' head, a dove descended from the heavens and a voice was heard to say, "This is my beloved son; listen to him." Ritual washings among the Jews implied a purification, and yet here a new beginning is divinely announced. It is in this context that Jesus' encounter with the Samaritan woman at Jacob's well must be understood. The Samaritans were Jewish religious outcasts. No self-respecting Jew would speak to any of them, much less to a woman of that race. Within minutes, Jesus transcended any such human limitations and revealed his own divine mission, identifying himself as the source of "living waters."

We have for many reasons chosen Ivan Mestrovic's splendid sculpture of *Christ At the Well With the Samaritan Woman* as one of the centerpieces of the Vatican Pavilion Exhibition. We have exercised a certain artistic liberty in having the "living waters" overflow the well, but this dramatically highlights the meaning of Christ's own words. The symbolism of "living waters," however, does not stop there. Later on in Jesus' public life, he began to preach and teach and to choose his apostles. Once, on the Sea of Galilee, he fell asleep in the boat with his apostles. Overcome with fear, the apostles awakened Jesus fearful that the ship might capsize and all perish. Jesus thereupon rebuked them with the words, "O you of little faith!" He calmed the seas and the winds and the apostles were in awe of his power.

This storm at sea was the basis of one of Giotto's famous mosaics in the "Navicella" of the old St. Peter's Church, now in the vestibule of the present Basilica of St. Peter's. Giotto also did a series of angels gazing at the scene; one of these appears in our collection. In subsequent generations, the incident of Jesus stilling the waters in the storm has become the symbol of the Barque of Peter making its way through time to the eternal harbor of salvation. Christ is always with the Church, always dwelling within the Church. Peter and his successors continue to be at the helm of the Barque of Peter. In the lovely processional cross on loan from the Treasury of *Notre Dame de Paris,* the Barque of Peter appears with Mary as the Star the Sea, and with St. Dominic and St. Bernadette celebrating the mysteries of Christ's death and resurrection as they are commemorated in the Rosary.

Jesus taught that unless people are baptized with water and the Spirit they cannot enter into the kingdom of God (John 3:5). The tradition of ritual ablutions was common among the Jews. The ritual was performed before entering the home and the temple and on other ceremonial occasions. One day, Jesus entered the house of a Pharisee, and remarked how the customary washing of a visitor's feet had been omitted. Washing the feet after a long day's journey was understandable, but there is more to it than that. Jesus uses the example of his washing of the feet on Holy Thursday as a special sign of his desire to teach his disciples how to serve one another. The humble act of washing feet was usually assigned to the lowest servant in the household. When Jesus rose from the table at the Last Supper and proceeded to wash the feet of the apostles, Peter protested. Jesus reminded him that unless he allowed him to wash his feet, he could have no part in his mission and his life. At this Peter said, "Then wash not only my feet but the whole of my body." Jesus' intent was to give to his closest associates, his own apostles, a dramatic reminder that they were to be in the service of one another in the humblest as well as in the most sublime of tasks.

Even at the moment of Christ's crucifixion and death, as captured by Raphael in the Sistine tapestry, and in El Greco's mystical interpretation, when Jesus has poured forth his last drop of blood, water is present. A Roman soldier plunges his spear into Christ's side, and water and blood pour forth. Closely associated in the Jewish tradition of the use of water as the source of purification was the ritual blood sacrifice of the temple. This obligation of offering blood sacrifice grew out of the tradition of the Covenant where, for certain sins, different blood sacrifices were to be offered. The offering of blood sacrifices in terms of turtle doves, lambs, or oxen depended upon the sins and the status and wealth of those offering the sacrifice. All of them were offered to wipe away the sins of the particular offending person or the sins of all the People of God. It is in this tradition that the lamb was offered on the Feast of Passover recalling the ancient night of liberation from Egyptian bondage. The lamb was offered in sacrifice and its blood splashed on the doorpost of the Jewish household to become a sign to the avenging angel to pass over the house and not to kill the eldest son of the Jewish family.

It is in this tradition that John the Baptist acclaimed Jesus as the Lamb of God who takes away the sins of the world. When Jesus died on the cross, he gave the last drop of his divine blood to wipe away all the sins of the world. Through this sacrifice, men and women of all time would benefit from the Savior's act of redemption.

Caravaggio has strikingly captured this moment in his *Deposition*. The sacrifice has been completed, and the body of the dead Christ is being lowered upon the slab where it will be anointed by John and Nicodemus.

John's finger reverently touches the wound in Christ's side from which the last drops of his blood had poured forth on Calvary, along with water.

The early Fathers of the Church commented upon this moment as the most significant one for the act of redemption; for it is at this moment that the sacrifice offered by Jesus to his father is completed in order that all men and women might be reconciled to him. Early Christian art delights in portraying the moment when the blood of Christ poured forth from his pierced side and was gathered into the chalice of salvation; the living torrents of water which issued from the Triumphant Cross, irrigated and watered the world with the grace of salvation. These rivulets of water often tapered off into seven distinct streams, symbolizing the early Christian understanding of the sacraments of the Church.

But it is only at the moment of Jesus' resurrection, joined to the moment of his death, that the fountains of living water pour forth from the side of the "wounded healer" in divinely transforming power. The moment of the resurrection is the most significant in time for it marks that moment in which Christ becomes the "firstborn" from the dead, the firstborn of the whole of the New Creation, the one "in whom" and "by whom" each one is healed and made new. The Raphael tapestry of the Risen Christ holding his banner, the sign of his conquest over death and sin, presents the New Adam, the head of the New Creation, in an absolutely unique interpretation of Christian art. It is the moment which recalls the words of Isaiah (Isaiah 12:3), "Then you shall draw water with joy from the well of the Savior," foreshadowing the words from John (7:37-39), "If any man thirst let him come to me and drink. He who believes in me, as the scripture says, 'rivers of living water shall flow from his bosom'." Jesus died that we might have life. He emptied himself of his divinity and became a man in order that he might make us like God himself. It is in the moment of the resurrection of Jesus that the ancient effects of eating the fruit of the tree of knowledge of good and evil are rectified by the fruit of the tree of the cross which becomes the body and blood of the risen Jesus Christ in the Bread of Life.

In the mystical tradition of the Church, the Holy Spirit becomes the celestial water supply which is "poured out upon us abundantly through Jesus Christ our Savior" (Titus 4:6). The Christian puts all of his trust in the Risen Christ who "baptizes in the Spirit"

(Mark 1:8) "and pours forth the Spirit" (Acts 7:15), like heavenly rain watering the dry ground of the soul. It is in this context of water, blood, and salvation that our Lord, himself, said of himself, "I am the resurrection and the life" (John 11:25).

The Church is therefore the continuation of the mystery of Christ's risen body extended into time and to all generations. The death and resurrection of Christ are sacramentally renewed each time the holy sacrifice of the Mass is offered. It is at the moment of the offering of the gifts of bread and wine and of their consecration that the mystery of Christ's risen presence is extended through time to all generations.

When Christ chose Peter and said, "You are Peter (Rock) and upon this rock I will build my Church," and when he subsequently told him that "I give to you the keys of the Kingdom of Heaven; and whatever you shall bind on earth shall be bound in heaven, and whatever you shall loose on earth shall be loosed in heaven," Peter and his successors become the rock out of which Christ continues in time. Peter is the mystical rock from which the waters of the New Testament bearing the fruitfulness of Christ's act of redemption flow. Christ is the new Moses of the New Creation which is the kingdom of God on earth, the Church. Thus, Peter and his successors take on an enormously important role in the history of the Church. The waters of eternal salvation are dispensed to the whole of the world through their ministry, and through them to all of those who have been born into Christ through the waters of baptism.

Recently, hidden under the Vatican hill, under St. Peter's itself, and not very far from the place where the tomb of St. Peter has been found, a living well has been discovered. It is a well like that of Jacob's, covered for centuries by church buildings that go back to the dawn of Christianity. Apparently, these springs are fed from sources deep within the rock of the Vatican hill. They provided refreshment for pagan ceremonies in the Circus of Nero, where tradition says Peter was crucified upside down. These same springs were channeled by the early Constantinian builders to provide waters for the pilgrims to wash in at the Great Cone Fountain at the center of the courtyard of Old St. Peter's. The vestige of this great fountain continues today in the two elegant fountains in the Piazza of St. Peter's.

The fabled Fountain of Youth is not an exotic far-away place. It is in reality hidden in the inner depths of the Church continuing in time, waiting to be tapped by believers and unbelievers alike. For the Christian believer who has been baptized with water and the Spirit, the wellspring of the mystical communing with the Risen Christ is planted in the souls of the faithful. Each Christian becomes in a very real sense "another Christ" continuing in time the work of redemption through the power of the Holy Spirit dwelling within him. Now the Lord uses our hands, our feet, our minds, and our hearts to make manifest the mystery which has been given to us at the moment of the pouring of the waters and the giving of the Spirit. The hidden mystical wellspring is the Church, and, like the ancient well of Jacob, we must uncover it anew so that all may come and be refreshed by the Risen Christ in his Church.

We hope these works of art in the Vatican Pavilion will help to uncover the wellspring of living faith within you and refresh your Judeo-Christian spirit in a deep and satisfying manner.

V.A.Mc

WATERWAYS AND MAPS

A SERIES OF beautiful maps reproduced from the Public Archives of Canada and the Macdonald-Stewart Foundation portray the advance of exploration in the New World and the gradual development of the Floridas and the Louisiana territories. The early routes of discovery were all waterways; the oceans, the seas and the rivers. The Atlantic Ocean, the Gulf of Mexico and the Mississippi River, were the passage ways that made the exploration and settlement of Louisiana and New Orleans possible.

Complementing our themes of "Living Waters and Evangelization," these maps graphically show how quickly settlements developed in the few short years from 1600 to 1740.

On loan from the Macdonald-Stewart Foundation and the National Map Collection, Public Archives of Canada, are the following early map renderings:

Map 1—The Old and New Worlds
The Dussemacker Map of 1600, 11″ × 14″
(The Macdonald-Stewart Foundation)

Map 2—The New World
The Jaillot Map of 1690, 21″ × 34″
(The Macdonald-Stewart Foundation)

Map 3—New France and The Mississippi
The Chatelaine Map of 1720, 21″ × 24¾″
(The National Map Collection, Public Archives, Canada)

Map 4—La Louisiane
The Homann Map of 1687, 19″ × 22″
(The Macdonald-Stewart Foundation)

Map 5—The Southern Coast of the New World
The deFer Map of 1701, 9½″ × 14½″
(The Macdonald-Stewart Foundation)

GALLERY ONE

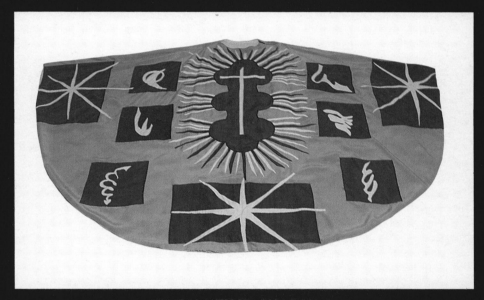

HENRI MATISSE, CHASUBLE

Map 1—The Old and New Worlds
The Dussemacker Map of 1600, 11″ × 14″
(The Macdonald-Stewart Foundation)

GALLERY ONE

The symbolism of "living waters" is found in Sacred Scripture. Christ proclaims to all, "He who believes in Me, as Scripture says, rivers of living water shall flow from his bosom" (John 7:37–39).
At the entrance gate of the New Testament, John the Baptist proclaims, "Behold the Lamb of God, behold him who taketh away the sins of the world" (John 1:25).

1) AUGUSTE RODIN; 1840-1916; **JOHN THE BAPTIST PREACHING;** 1879; bronze; height 84″. *Philadelphia Museum of Art, Rodin Museum,* Philadelphia, Pennsylvania. Gift of Jules E. Mastbaum.

At the entrance gate of the New Testament, we see John the Baptist standing on the bank of the Jordan River and pointing with his finger to Christ, saying, "Behold the Lamb of God, behold him who takes away the sins of the world" (John 1:25).

"I baptize with water, but there is one coming after

19

me who will baptize with water and the spirit" (Mark 1:8).

Rodin said of his own art: "I have invented nothing. I only rediscover . . ." In this celebrated rendering of John the Baptist, Rodin rediscovers the spirit of the preacher announcing the word of God to all who will hear. As such, the word has an eternal quality to it. Each day is an acceptable day of salvation. The statue is saying, as it were, "Let those who have ears, hear!"

V.A.Mc.

2) THE PELICAN AND ITS YOUNG; 1830; wood and gold leaf; height 17″, width 13¼″. The School of Quévillon; *Musée du Québec*, Quebec City, Canada

A beautifully carved pelican piercing its own breast to feed its young. From ancient times, it was used as a symbol for Christ shedding his blood for the redemption of mankind. In Louisiana, it was adopted as the symbol for the State, not only because of its great natural abundance but also for its religious symbolism. This work is now on exhibition in the Louisiana Catholic Church section.

V.A.Mc.

3A) MISSAL; Spain, 19th century; paper, velvet cover with handwork of gold and silver, precious stones and enamel; height 16⁹⁄₁₆″, width 11¾″. *Sacristy, Sistine Chapel,* Vatican City

3B) LECTERN; Italy 19th—20th century; gilded copper and painted enamel; height 12⅝″ closed (22″ open), width 15¾″, depth 11¾″. *Sacristy, Sistine Chapel,* Vatican City

Valuable hand-crafted work in intaglio. In the center of the front side is the image of the Holy Cross of Jesus painted on enamel. Two other medallions of enamel with the symbol of the Lamb are in the center of the two frontal columns which emerge from the body.

G.M.

4) JEANNE LeBER; 1662–1714; **ALTAR ANTEPENDIUM;** Montreal—beginning of eighteenth century; silver, gold and silk thread on satin. On loan from the Treasury of the Cathedral of *Notre Dame de Montréal,* Canada

On the front cover is a large silver cross in whose center are images in colored enamel of the Sacred Heart of Jesus and whose four corners bear the images of the four Evangelists. In the center is a circle of twelve stars. The surrounding frame of gilded silver extends to the four corners of the medallions with etched scenes relating to the evangelization of the four continents: Europe, Asia, Africa and America. The first medallion at the top left depicts the "Visions of Constantine," while the last, in the lower left, depicts the "Landing of Columbus in the New World." The evangelization of Oceania appears just below the center. Above the center appears the enamel crest of His Holiness, Leo XIII.

On the back cover is the episcopal crest with the dedication, "To His Holiness, Pope Leo XIII. The Diocese of Cuenca."

On the spine is the indication of the workshop which executed the covers: *"El Arte Cristiano."*

Given by the Diocese of Cuenca, in Spain, to Leo XIII, on the occasion of his 50th anniversary of ordination to the priesthood.

G.M.

In the early seventeenth century, Canada often acted as a magnet, drawing people from France to the new world. A small group of Ursuline nuns felt the call to mission and to teach in Canada so strongly that, in 1639, they left their cloisters in France. Under the indomitable leadership of Marie de l'Incarnation, they set off on a 2,500-mile journey across a most unpleasant ocean to the colony of New France. It took them three months to reach their destination, Quebec, which, at the time consisted of only 250 people, was perched precariously on the edge of a vast wilderness. After a brief flurry of welcome, the sisters retired into their cloister and set about fulfilling the teaching mission that had originally inspired them. In their small school they taught both French and Indian girls. A letter written by Marie de l'Incarnation in 1640 gives us a picture of what the teaching was like. Speaking of a young Indian girl, she says, "She has made very great progress with us in the knowledge of the mysteries, and, as well, in good manners, embroidery, reading, playing the viola, and a thousand other little skills." At that time, any well-brought-up young lady in France would have been taught embroidery and, with the coming of the Ursulines, so it was in Canada. The sisters were fully equipped to both teach and practice the art of fine embroidery, and naturally the churches in the new country needed adorning. Along with all the other duties, the Ursuline sisters managed to produce many beautiful ecclesiastical hangings and vestments and, as time went on, their embroidery became a way of providing support for their new convents.

A young woman named Jeanne LeBer went to the Ursuline Convent in Quebec in 1675 to pursue her education. It was while she was a student with the Ursuline sisters that she learned embroidery. By 1677, she returned to Montreal and took private vows with the Congregation of *Notre Dame*. She spent the rest of her life designing and executing ecclesiastical embroideries. One such embroidery is the magnificent Holy Spirit antependium which we have on loan from the Treasury of *Notre Dame de Montréal*. The center piece of the frontal is a beautiful gold and silver Holy Spirit in the shape of a dove. Emanating from the dove are the unfolding of the embroidered roses and a Greek cross, or a cross of St. Andrew. The detail of the embroidery and the imaginative coloration are simply magnificent and a tribute to the artistry of this young French-Canadian.

D.K.B.

---

5) LITURGICAL VESTMENTS; The Evangelization Vestments of St. Francis of Assisi; France, before 1926; gold, silk and handworked embroidery. *Sacristy, Sistine Chapel,* Vatican City

Multicolored hand-made embroidery with innumerable scenes related to the life of St. Francis of Assisi and of the principal Franciscan saints, as well as salient episodes in the missionary history of the Franciscan Order.

This work was done by the Claretians of the monastery of Mazamat d'Albi in France, and donated by the Third Order Franciscan to His Holiness Pius XI on the occasion of the celebration of the eighth centennial of the death of the Saint of Poverty (1226–1926).

The vestments consist of:

A. Chasuble (cloak worn by the priest for the celebration of the Mass). Height at shoulders 43¼″ (at the center 41¾″), width 27½″

B. Maniple (which the priest formerly wore on the left arm) Height 43¼″ (including fringe, 47½″), width 5½″ (in widest part) 3⅞″ (in narrowest part)

C. Stole (which the priest wears on his shoulders under the chasuble) Height 80″ (with fringe, 86½″), width 5½″

D. Veil (placed on the chalice to cover it) Height 21¼″, width 21¼″

G.M.

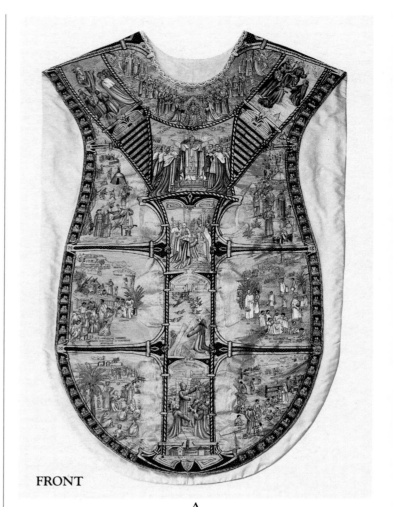

FRONT

A.

BACK

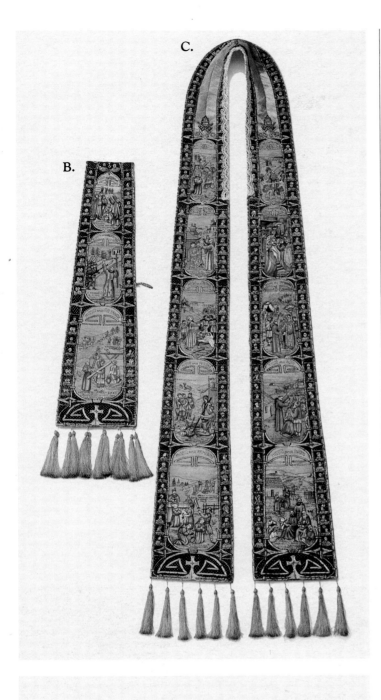

C.

B.

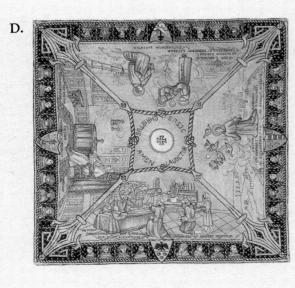

D.

5) MITRE; Italy, 19th century (before ca. 1854); gold, silver, satin; height 14³⁄₁₆″, width 13″, length of the stays 16½″. *Sacristy, Sistine Chapel,* Vatican City

On the front is the Good Shepherd amidst palms and lambs; on the back the Immaculate Conception is between two genuflecting angels; on the stays, embroidered with diverse floral motifs, two polychrome crests of Pius IX, placed at the extremities.

Offered to His Holiness Pius IX on the occasion of the solemn definition of the dogma of the Immaculate Conception, in the Vatican Basilica, December 8, 1854.

G.M.

7) CROSIER; Bavaria, 19th century (before 1853); ivory, metal and gems (amethyst and topaz); height 80⅝", width 5½". *Sacristy, Sistine Chapel,* Vatican City

At the top of the crosier is the Virgin, crowned, holding the Child. Below, in four niches, in imitation Gothic style, are Saints Rupert, Benno, and Borginian (particularly honored in Bavaria), and Charles Borromeo.

Beneath is a small shield, dated 1853; on the sides of the shield are the letters C A (*Carolus Augustus*); still farther down is AE MF. The whole Latin inscription reads: "Given to His Holiness, Pius IX, by Cardinal Karl August von Reisach, first Bishop of Eichstatt, and later, of Munich and Freising."

G.M.

8) RELIQUARY OF ST. FRANCIS XAVIER; Goa (India), 17th century; silver and precious stones; height 12¼" (including the base, 14³⁄₁₆"), width 10⁷⁄₁₆" (with the base, 12¼") thickness, 1⁹⁄₁₆". *Sacristy, Sistine Chapel,* Vatican City

This is an artistic work in silver filigree and precious stones, reproducing the silver sarcophagus, gift of Ferdinando II de Medici, Grand Duke of Tuscany. It contains the incorrupt body of Saint Francis Xavier, Apostle of India and Japan; Goa (India), the Church of Buon Gesù. A relic of the saint is preserved behind the grill opening in the center. The work was executed in Goa.

G.M.

9) HENRI MATISSE; 1869–1954; **CHASUBLE;** Vence, France, 1952; linen and wool, height 72″, width 72″. *Chapelle du Rosaire*, Vence, France

In 1951, the great contemporary French master, Henri Matisse, completed the *Chapelle du Rosaire* for the Second Order of Contemplative Dominican Sisters. He designed and executed the whole chapel, from the exquisite stained glass windows and the carving on the door of the confessional, to the gold candelabra on the altar and chasubles used during the liturgy.

This chasuble—one of several which Matisse designed—is called the Gaudete Chasuble because it was meant to be worn on the Third Sunday of Advent. On this day the Church, putting aside the somber Advent color, uses instead a rose-colored vestment whose softer hue combines colors symbolic of both penance and joy. This chasuble is eloquent in expressing the hope and expectation connected with the coming feast of the birth and rebirth of Christ at Christmas. The design on the chasuble depicts the cross with the symbols of the wounds emanating radiant light. The colors are rose, white and blue; rose, symbolizing joy in the triumph of the cross and the rebirth of Christ; blue as a reference to the Virgin; and white as the symbol of purity and salvation.

Plans for this chapel were begun in the autumn of 1947, when Matisse was seventy-seven years of age. He intended it as a gift of gratitude to a member of the Community who had cared for him in his arthritic condition. The chapel was blessed by Bishop Réymond on June 25, 1951.

A chasuble is a vestment worn by the priest at Mass. It hangs in heavy folds, constantly changing form as the priest moves, and symbolizes in diverse colors the liturgical seasons of the year.

V.A.Mc.

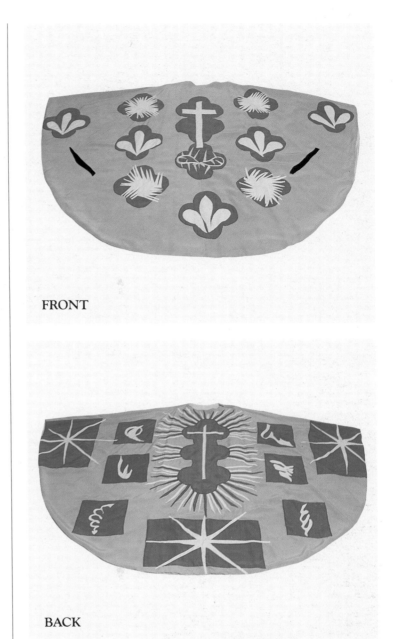

FRONT

BACK

10) TYMPANUM OF ST. LOUIS KING OF FRANCE; late 13th or early 14th century, c. 1325; carved stone; height 40⅛″, width 50⅜″. *Musée Carnavalet*, Paris, France

This remarkable high-relief sculpture in stone is one of the earliest known depictions of St. Louis and his wife, Blanche of France, kneeling at his side. It was removed from the old *Convent des Cordeliers* in order to preserve it. A priceless work of the high Gothic period, it is on special loan to the New Orleans Vatican Pavilion through the *Patrimoine* of France.

St. Louis is the Patron Saint of the Archdiocese of New Orleans and of our own Cathedral. The loan of this sculpture represents a special bond of friendship between old and new France.

V.A.Mc.

**11) LEO MOL; SCULPTURED BUST OF HIS HOLINESS
POPE JOHN PAUL II;** 1979; bronze; height 32″, width 24″.
On loan from the Collection of His Eminence G. Emmett
Cardinal Carter of Toronto, Canada

This sculptured portrait of His Holiness by the Canadian sculptor, Leo Mol, was commissioned by the Vatican. This second casting was presented on the 22nd
of October, 1979, by Premier William Davis on behalf
of the people of Ontario, Canada, to Cardinal Carter.
The bust captures the wit, charm and intelligence of
the Holy Father. A high degree of technical and artistic
skill produces an effective portrait bust. A prophetic
Polish poet wrote in 1840:

*In the midst of the confusion
God has Sounded a great bell . . .
It is to a Slavic Pope
that he has opened the access
to the Throne of Thrones
He will reveal God as clear as the light of day . . .
See! He comes the Slavic Pope
the Brother of All Nations*

JULIUSZ SLOWACKI, 1840

V.A.Mc.

GALLERY TWO

PROCESSIONAL CROSS

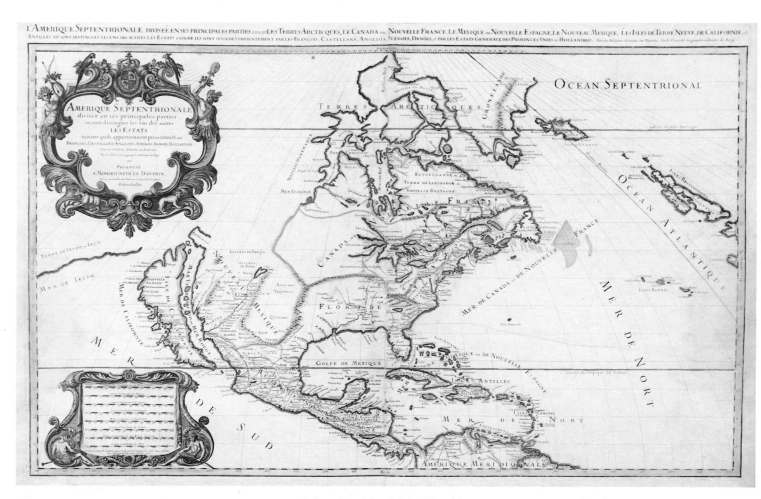

Map 2—The New World
The Jaillot Map of 1690, 21″ × 34 ″
(The Macdonald-Stewart Foundation)

"If you knew who it was who is speaking to you, you would ask of him and he would have given you living waters to spring up inside of you to life everlasting" (John 4:10).

12) THE BARQUE OF ST. PETER; with the Virgin, St. Dominic and St. Bernadette; mid 19th century; gold bronze and inlaid mosaic; height 84″, width 18″. *Treasury of Notre Dame de Paris, France*

A processional cross celebrating 643 years of the rosary, 1215–1858. It depicts the Virgin Mary standing in the center of the barque of St. Peter with her emblem on the sails as the Star of the Sea. The ancient tradition of the Church maintains that Mary gave the rosary to St. Dominic Guzman, here depicted kneeling on her right hand side. On the left is shown St. Bernadette of Lourdes reciting her rosary during the apparitions at Lourdes. The mast is topped by a crown mounted with a French cross showing the fleurs de lis emanating from the ends of the cross.

The Dominicans follow the medieval custom of meditating on the joys, sorrows and triumphs of Christ's life, death and resurrection. While St. Bernadette of Lourdes recited her rosary, Mary appeared to her and revealed herself as the "Immaculate Con-

ception". Following the instructions of Mary, Bernadette scratched the ground where she was kneeling and a spring of living waters flowed up. These have become the healing waters of Lourdes.

V.A.Mc.

13) ENFANT JESUS AU GLOBE; 18th century; polychromed wood; height 15⁹⁄₁₆″. *Musée du Québec*, Quebec City, Canada

A charming French-Canadian Infant Jesus holding the globe of the world in his left hand and giving a benediction with his right. It resembles similar works, one of which is in the National Gallery of Canada. This polychromed sculpture epitomizes the best in French-Canadian sculpture and is on loan from the *Musée du Québec*.

V.A.Mc.

14) TOMMASO GISMONDI; **MADONNA OF CZESTOCHOWA;** 20th century; silvered bronze with gold shadings (the face and hands of the Virgin and Child are painted in black); height 37⅞″, width 26″, thickness 1⁹⁄₁₆″. *Floreria Apostolica,* Vatican City

The bas-relief reproduces the famous icon of the Black Madonna honored in the sanctuary of Jasna Góra, in Poland.

The work was offered by the artist to His Holiness John Paul II on the occasion of the presentation of the bronze doors of the church of *St. Pierre de Montmartre* in Paris. This Madonna represents one of the great devotions the Polish people have to Mary, the Mother of God.

G.M.

---

15) PAUL LAMBERT DIT SAINT-PAUL; 1691–1749; **HOLY WATER FONT;** Québec City; silver; height 6⅞″; signed. *National Gallery of Canada,* Ottawa, Canada

Paul Lambert was the most prolific Québec silversmith of the first half of the eighteenth century and the first to earn his livelihood entirely through his craft. Although he received numerous church commissions his chief clientele was the *petite bourgeoisie,* whose requirements were usually limited to bowls, tumblers, and flatware, as the wealthier gentlemen-bourgeois preferred to order from the more prestigious Parisian workshops.

This is a small silver holy water font used to bless oneself when entering or leaving a chapel or a room. It is simply designed with the Corpus and the inscription above, INRI, *Jesus Nazarenus Rex Judeorum,* Jesus of Nazareth, King of the Jews. Holy water fonts continue the ancient tradition of purification and cleansing which goes back to Old Testament time. They are used to this day in all Roman Catholic churches and in many Catholic homes.

R.A.F.

This is a long-standing artistic device to symbolize the radiance of divinity. Immediately above the lunette, is a primitive crucifix in silver. The embellishment of the monstrance follows the tradition of the day with angels and angel wings holding the design together at the base, with very fine silver hammered designs.

V.A.Mc.

17) JACQUES PAGÉ; 1682–1742; **CIBORIUM;** c. 1725; silver; height 11″. *The National Gallery of Canada*, Ottawa, Canada

This chaste silver ciborium, designed to hold the consecrated hosts, is an excellent example of early French-Canadian silver. The top of the ciborium has a cross with the indication of the fleur de lis, symbol of France, as well as of purity. The beauty of the ciborium is in the simpleness of the design, relatively unadorned.

V.A.Mc.

16) PAUL LAMBERT DIT SAINT-PAUL; 1691–1749; **MONSTRANCE;** 1735; silver; height 17½″. *National Gallery of Canada*, Ottawa, Canada

The Roman Catholic church played an enormously important role in early French-Canadian history. It was established, stable, and provided craftsmen with a demanding patron. Because so many of the Church rituals were based on a desire to enhance the significance of the liturgical actions, especially those connected with the celebration of the Mass and the adoration of the Christ in the Bread of Life, it became fashionable for many religious articles to be made out of silver and gold.

This silver monstrance is part of the Henry Birks Collection of Canadian silver, given in 1979 to the National Gallery of Canada. It represents one of the finest pieces of silver worked in the mid-eighteenth century. The monstrance is used to display the consecrated bread in the circular area, sometimes called the lunette, with radiant spokes emanating from the circle.

18) FRANÇOIS RANVOYZÉ; 1739–1819; **CENSER AND BOAT;** silver; height 8⅜″. *National Gallery of Canada,* Ottawa, Canada

The formative years of New France were occupied with survival. Since silver- and gold-making flourished best under patronage, the early French-Canadian gold- and silver-smiths had to wait for more tranquil times before establishing businesses. At the beginning of the 18th century, the fur trade expanded, bringing with it a degree of prosperity and permanence, which in turn encouraged settled communities. Trading posts were soon established and small but important towns, such as Québec, Montréal and Trois Rivières, developed into expanding urban centers. The Roman Catholic Church widened its administrative jurisdiction, and the wheels of colonial administration were set in motion. This was the cultural milieu required for the gold and silver trade.

Public records of the sixteen hundreds make reference to several silversmiths. No examples of their work have been found. However, many silver and some gold objects made in the early seventeen hundreds do exist. These were produced by prosperous and well-known artisans busy working for their patrons, in particular, the Roman Catholic Church. Their work was comparable to some of the best made in France and stylistically resembled gold and silver from there. As a result, the patterns found on the chalices, ciboriums, and monstrances are closely associated with silver of the Louis XIV and Louis XV periods.

On the other hand, with the passing of time, style changes took place but none of the gold- or silver-smiths working during this period surpassed Ranvoyzé. Francois Ranvoyzé (1739–1819) has rightly been considered by many to be Canada's outstanding gold- and silversmith, for he developed a beaten technique that made his work both beautiful and distinctive.

By special permission from the National Gallery of Canada, the *Musée du Québec,* and the *Musée de Moncton* we have on loan a cross section of the silver and gold works which illustrates the best works in their collections.

T.N.

The censer is used on solemn occasions to symbolize the prayers and the worship of the faithful ascending to God. Incense placed over burning charcoal produces a fragrant aroma, and the rising clouds of smoke symbolize the prayers which rise heavenwards. This is a particularly well-designed silver censer. The openings through the floral design enable the smoke to escape into the surrounding area. The garland design draped around the base of the censer gives it a delicate touch.

V.A.Mc.

19) FRANÇOIS RANVOYZÉ; 1739–1819; SANCTUARY LAMP; silver; height 12". *National Gallery of Canada, Ottawa, Canada*

Another beautiful piece in the Birks Collection of Canadian silver, given to the National Gallery of Canada in 1979 illustrates the elaborateness of silver-making. This lamp was designed to hang in the center of the sanctuary with a perpetually burning light to symbolize the presence of the Lord in the Blessed Sacrament. This is an excellent example of hammered Canadian silver used for ecclesiastical purposes.

V.A.Mc.

---

20) FRANÇOIS RANVOYZÉ; 1739–1819; CHALICE; silver; height 79½"; signed and dated. *National Gallery of Canada, Ottawa, Canada*

A particularly fine silver chalice showing the elegance of plain-surfaced silver juxtaposed with highly hammered floral areas. The chalice combines an elegance of design with an elaborate low relief. Such chalices are used in the liturgy of the Mass to celebrate the Bread of Life.

V.A.Mc.

21) ALTAR CROSS; Rome, 1489; silver, partly gilt, and niello; height 16⅞". *Biblioteca Apostolica Vaticana, Museo Sacro,* Vatican City

The main decorative elements of the cross are the silver filigree scrolls applied on both sides, serving as foils for the hollow, cast-silver figures: Christ, flanked by two mourning Marys and by the Magdalene, repeated twice, in the top and bottom quatrefoils. A motif of Saint Andrew's crosses appears along the edges of the cross. On the back of the cross, the four lobed medallions have lost their decoration, which, judging from the hatched ground of two of them, must have been painted in translucent enamel. The provenance of the cross is not known, but the allusion to Saint Andrew suggests that it may come from Saint Peter's, where, until 1606, the head of the apostle, one of the most important relics in the basilica, was kept in an altar tabernacle erected by Pius II (1458–64).

Incised on the front and back of the shaft of the cross is the following dedicatory inscription: *GENTILIS * DE * SANCTIS/DOCTOR/DONAVIT/* A * APLO/DEI/AHO/MCCCC/LXXXVIIII/ROM* (Given by Doctor Gentile de Sanctis to God's Apostle in 1489 Rome).

O. R.

33

FRONT

BACK

22) PROCESSIONAL CROSS; sheets of enameled copper on a bore of wood; 13th century; height 1¾″, width 14³⁄₁₆″; restored 1983. Treasury of *Lyons Cathedral*, France

Front: Gold-colored copper globes at the extremities of this cross. Plaques at the bottom, blue enamel strewn with roses and nails. At the intersection, a solemn Christ (engraved in the 19th century to replace the Christ in relief; the original has disappeared). At the extremities, the symbols of the four Evangelists, with heads in relief (one head is missing).

Back: The middle part of the arms of the cross is covered with embossed silver plates depicting a sowing or scattering of fleurs-de-lis between two bands of borders. At the juncture and ends the sheets of copper enameled in deep blue represent the Paschal Lamb; at the lateral extremities, two St. Johns (one molded from the other); above, an angel with open wings; below, same.

From the Collection of Cardinald Bonald. Restored in the 19th century.

T.F.

23) IVAN MESTROVIC; 1883–1966; **CHRIST AND THE SAMARITAN WOMAN AT JACOB'S WELL;** 1957; bronze; height 7¼′, width 2½′. Specially recast from The Collection of the O'Shaughnessy Hall Courtyard, *Snite Museum, University of Notre Dame*, Notre Dame, Indiana

Ivan Mestrovic is an internationally famous Yugoslav sculptor. He was deeply committed to the Bible, to God, and to the fulfillment of his own artistic talent. His magnificent and powerful creations of *Moses, Job,* and *Jesus,* and his touching renditions of the *Virgin and Child,* reveal him to be a man of profound faith. He once said:
"We peasants who have learned to follow the plow . . . hope that the harvest time will give us wheat, at least enough grain for seed. We must have faith."

Mestrovic's faith in God and in man is felt unmistakably in all his artistic productions.

Mestrovic spent the last twenty years of his life at the University of Notre Dame, in South Bend, Indiana, where he produced some of his greatest works, both as an artist and as a believer. By 1957, he had completed his larger-than-life bronze group, *Christ and the Samaritan Woman at Jacob's Well.* He had explored this theme as far back as 1927, when he did a wood-relief of it for his family at the Mestrovic chapel in Split, Yugoslavia.

This work of Mestrovic was selected above all the others to be the centerpiece of the Vatican Pavilion at the New Orleans World Fair. It fits in well with the Fair's overall theme: "The Source of Living Waters." It is high tribute to Mestrovic that one of his best works has been given so prominent a place.

The Notre Dame work demonstrates his mastery of gestures, poses, form, and human relationships. All of

these aspects he brought together here. A relaxed Christ sits on the edge of a granite well. The Samaritan woman, holding her vase, is positioned in a graceful S-pattern, her head bent towards the well. She does not look directly at Jesus. She mentions the Messiah, and Christ says to her, "I who am speaking to you, am he" (John 4:1–26). Rarely do we meet a more human Christ in the Gospels, and seldom do we perceive how dynamically he interacted with people.

In an interview given to Dr. Dean Porter of the Snite Museum of Art at Notre Dame, Father Theodore M. Hesburgh, C.S.C., President of the University of Notre Dame, explained how this work came into existence:

"The *Woman at the Well* came forth from Mestrovic's whole being. He had done some sketches of this scene as every other sculptor has done . . . In any event, it was a theme that was in his mind . . ."

Father Hesburgh continued:

"The *Woman at the Well* came about in an interesting way. I wanted a well out in the courtyard, so I called his wife, Olga, one day and asked her what I had to do to induce her husband to sculpt us a well, and she replied, 'Invite us to dinner at the Morris Inn.' This I did, and the three of us had lunch. Towards the end of lunch, I asked, 'What are you working on now, Maestro?' He explained that he was working on a he-

roic-size corpus for a crucifix. I then said, 'I have always hoped that you might one day do some figures for a well in the courtyard outside your studio.' At this, Olga broke in, saying, 'Ivan, I have always wanted you to do a fountain.' He then said, without any hesitation, 'I will do the Samaritan Woman at the Well.' And that was that."

Few artists have articulated their insights as well as Mestrovic. Responding to the reception of the Christian Culture Award in 1954, at Windsor, Canada, he said:

"Evil cannot be thwarted with evil; harmony does not arise from sowing discord, preaching hatred. War, regardless of who wages it, is a common evil reducing man to the status of half-animal, destructive of all human values, material and spiritual.

Perplexed and confused, I returned to a small neutral country to try to find, at least, a solution to my personal spiritual problem.

With me I took the book which in my childhood I had read without a great deal of understanding; only the memory of its poetic beauty had still lingered in my mind. But now I understood it: I knew then that this book contained not only unmatched beauty but also the profoundest wisdom. The book was the New Testament.

Inspired by the great drama of the Son of God becoming Flesh, I started to work on themes taken from the life of Jesus of Nazareth. It was then that I carved in wood the scene of the Crucifixion. Many people did not like it, because it was not aesthetically pleasing. They found the Crucified Christ too emaciated and disfigured. But the Crucifixion scene was not meant to represent the historical Jesus nor his supreme sacrifice. It was intended to depict the crucifixion of his idea, the perversion and disfiguration of the teachings for which he came into this world and for which he died on the Cross.

There are many people today who have reached the conviction that one main cause of the tragic events of the recent past, and of those which loom on the horizon, is the fact that contemporary man has all but forgotten the great teachings of the Sermon on the Mount. For this blame rests not only on our contemporary despotisms, but, unfortunately, on a long list of talented men of science and art who have not foreseen the corroding implications and destructive consequences of their doctrines. This atmosphere of unbelief, this tragic state of man isolated from the very axis which holds and moves everything, has had repercussions on all domains of human activity, including art, which in the most significant periods of civilization worked hand in hand with religion—an ennobling and spiritualizing factor in human life.

Christian civilization, in our days, finds itself locked in a mortal struggle with the forces of secularism in varying forms and degrees. Too many people still fail to realize that Christianity, by waging the fight for its principles, defends also the foundations of the democratic way of life: For the concept of the dignity of each man and the equality of all men stands and falls with the Judeo Christian view that man is created in the image of God. Thus the Church is in the front lines of the battle against the onslaughts on human freedom.

. . . In vain do the godless and restless men, who are today making weapons in the hope of enslaving the world, think that the trunk of the Christian tree is withered. It will outlive and outlast the forces of evil in my native land and throughout the whole world. He who has conquered death will conquer the destruction of His teaching.

I am happy and grateful that my modest artistic efforts have been considered a contribution to Christian culture, which I would define with Paul as consisting of three things: faith, love and hope. Faith in God, love of him and our fellowmen and the hope of final victory of good and evil."

V.A.Mc.

24) ETHIOPIAN CROSS; 16th century; silver, height 18", width 9". Treasury of *Notre Dame de Paris*, France

A well-designed filigree cross showing the interlacing motif common to Ethiopian crosses. This particular cross was given to the Treasury of *Notre Dame de Paris* by the Emperor Haile Selassie and is on loan from the Treasury of *Notre Dame de Paris*.

V.A.Mc.

25) CRUCIFIX; Zaire; Bakongo people; 17th century; bronze; height 15¾", maximum width, 7½". *Pontificio Museo Missionario-Etnologico,* Vatican City

The cross was introduced to the Lower Congo region by the first Portuguese missionaries in the fifteenth century. By the sixteenth century, crosses had begun to be manufactured in Africa. Initially, these crosses imitated European examples, but over time they were transformed into completely African works.

This cross must have been made toward the end of the seventeenth century, when stylistic and ideological transformations had become resolved. It was collected by Redemptorist fathers in the Lower Congo and sent from Brussels to the Vatican in 1924 for the *Esposizione Missionaria* in 1925.

The image is that of an African Christ: curly hair, broad nose, and protruding navel. His outstretched arms, crossed feet, prominent ribs, and loin cloth tied in a knot on one side reflect a European model. This is a Christ who is not yet dead. His head is not bent, and his chest has not been pierced.

The female figure at the bottom is surely the Madonna. Opinions are very diverse regarding the identities of the other three. The Trinity, three apostles, souls of the dead saved by Christ and on their way to heaven, relatives who mourn the dying Christ—all are possible explanations but may not be accurate.

J.P.

26) FRANÇOIS RANVOYZÉ; 1739–1819; **A PROCESSIONAL CROSS MADE FOR THE OLD LORETTO CHURCH;** the end of the eighteenth century; silver; height 24⅛″. *Musée du Québec*, Quebec City, Canada

This unique silver processional cross has the usual crucifixion on one side, but on the reverse side has a small shrine to the Virgin and Christ Child. It has a particularly well-chiseled light design, especially with the fleur-de-lis at the ends of the cross. It is one of the best silver processional crosses to survive from that period.

V.A.Mc.

27) **THE CHRIST RELIQUARY;** early 12th century; polychromed olive wood with braided silk and gold thread; height 9″, width 9″. *St. Michel d'Aiguille, Le Puy, Haûte-Loire,* France

A small portable cross, the ends adorned with two lobes, polychromed. Blue with red border, yellow dots (stipple), lacking the title on the cross. Christ is shown with arms extended horizontally, in majesty, in the Byzantine manner popularized by the Holy Face of Lucca (Lucques). The head is large (⅕th the height of the whole) painted in the natural color. The hands are also painted in flesh color and the open thumbs are unusual. The eyes are very large, opened wide, dark blue, like the hair, moustache and pointed beard. The feet are parallel and rest on a platform for support. The body of Christ is quite straight, covered with a blue robe with long vertical pleats. The robe is held at the waist by a gold sash knotted in front. The long sleeves reach the wrist and are adorned, like the hem of the robe, with a braid of gold thread and silk. The design is geometric. A small reliquary cavity has been worked into the wood. The overall effect is one of a very Byzantine priestly character.

Found in 1955, along with other objects, inside two copper trays (or plates) under a fragment of an ancient column located in the center of the original altar of the chapel. It is supposed to have been a souvenir brought back from a pilgrimage to Constantinople and Mount Gargan in southern Italy.

T.F.

28) CORPUS CHRISTI; 16th century; ivory; height 20″, width 18″. Treasury of *Notre Dame de Paris,* France

This is an exquisitely carved French ivory of the body of Christ. It has been in the Treasury of *Notre Dame de Paris* and is one of the prized works of the collection. It is superbly carved and reflects the elegance of style and sensitive faith of the unknown artist.

V.A.Mc.

---

29) BANDELE OF OSILLORIN; Yoruba, Nigeria; **DOOR PANEL;** 1964; wood; height 84″. *African Art Museum of the Society of African Missions,* Tenafly, New Jersey.

Illustrated here is one of the four large wood panels which flank the two entrances to the African museum. They were carved in 1964 by Bandele of Osillorin. Bandele is the son of Areogun, who was known as one of the greatest of Yoruba traditional carvers. Bandele was himself a traditional carver before beginning around 1948 to carve Christian subjects on commission from Fr. Kevin Carroll, S.M.A. The top frieze of this panel portrays the annunciation with Mary engaged in the daily routine of pounding yams in a mortar. The middle scene represents the flight into Egypt. On the bottom Christ is flanked by two Yoruba cult-priests. The Oshanyin herbalist on the left holds a wrought-iron staff surmounted with birds in one hand and a horn to hold the medicine he makes against insanity and witchcraft in the other. On the right is a priest of Shango with his oshe, or double-headed axe, and his shere, or rattle.

W.S.

GALLERY THREE

THE CHAMPAGNE MADONNA AND CHILD (detail)

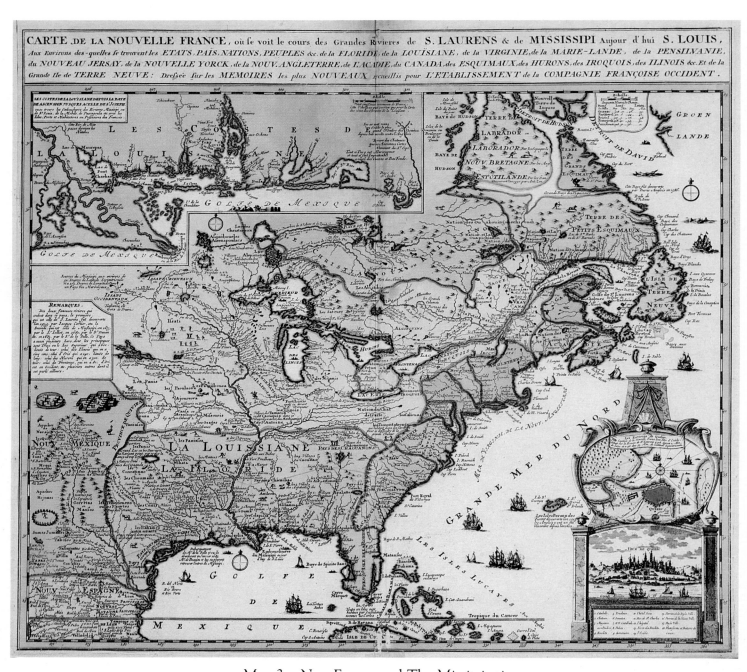

Map 3—New France and The Mississippi
The Chatelaine Map of 1720, 21″ × 24¾″
(The National Map Collection, Public Archives,
Canada)

"Then you shall draw water with joy from the well of the Savior" (Isaiah 12:3).

30) BERNARD & GRUNNING; **EUCHARISTIC CONGRESS MONSTRANCE;** 1938; gold, silver and precious jewels; height 42". *Archdiocese of New Orleans, Louisiana*

A special ostensorium was designed for the VIIIth National Eucharistic Congress held in New Orleans in 1938.

Towards the close of 1937, Miss Marie Bunol, of St. Rita's Parish in New Orleans, proposed that individuals from the south should contribute jewelry or precious stones for the creation of this Eucharistic monstrance. Her idea was that people should make some direct sacrifice so that the finished piece would represent actual personal gifts of individuals. She initiated the suggestion by contributing some of her own jewelry. Her idea was enthusiastically endorsed by the Archdiocesan Council of Catholic Women. A wedding ring, the chalice of a deceased priest, a baby's gold cup, a tiny ring, an ancient gold chain, family heirlooms, diamond pendants from Victorian times, a gold nugget from the days of '49, an aged woman's last bit of gold jewelry—in all, the gifts symbolized the love and sentiment, the tragedy and affection of human life through the years. The gifts came from as far away as Quebec City and New York. The final inventory included an amazing assemblage of gold, silver and platinum jewelry, and articles containing diamonds, pearls, rubies and other precious stones. Over 5,000 persons contributed materials out of which this monstrance was created.

The monstrance is composed of three parts: the *gloria,* the *shaft,* and the *base.* The *gloria,* or halo design, front and back, includes seven rays on different planes. Directly around the luna is a diamond ray made up of 231 brilliant diamonds. Adjoining it is the shield ray which bears 13 coats of arms in colored enamel. The one at the top center depicts the symbols of the priest—chalice, stole and missal.

The 12 other coats of arms bear the shields of the 12 nations that have provided priests to Louisiana and have thus perpetuated the Bread of Life in our midst. The nations represented are the United States, Canada, France, Spain, Italy, Germany, Switzerland, Austria, Belgium, Holland, Ireland and Luxemberg. Angels on each side support this ray.

The next ray shows the main theme of the monstrance. This is called the procession ray. On a circular embossed gold plaque is depicted the first important Eucharistic Congress ever held in New Orleans. This occurred on the 17th of July, 1734, when the Ursuline nuns moved from their temporary quarters in Bienville's old home to their new permanent convent on Chartres and Ursulines Streets. One of the nuns taking part in the famous procession, carrying the Blessed Sacrament to their new chapel, left a written account of the ceremony. This historic document was used as the basis for depicting the event on the *gloria* of the ostensorium. Bienville, the founder of New Orleans, and then Governor of the Louisiana Colony, is shown leading the procession, accompanied by Colonial officials, followed by prominent leaders of the city carrying lighted candles, convent girls, clergy and, finally, the Capuchin pastor of New Orleans carrying the Blessed Sacrament under an arched canopy. Along the procession route is a file of soldiers with muskets, acting as a guard of honor. All the figures are in low relief and are clearly discernible.

At the base of this ray, is an embossed circular representation of the official Eucharistic Congress emblem showing the pelican feeding its young with the chalice and the Bread of Life superimposed on the breast of the pelican. The theme "the Way, the Truth and the Life," encompasses the design. At the outer edges are the *Alpha* and the *Omega* (the first and last letters of the Greek alphabet), representing Christ as the beginning and end of all things.

Next is a flat gold ray that emphasizes the processional ray in relief. The outer ray is made up of spikes and stylized wheat stalks symbolizing the Bread of Life. Surmounting the monstrance is a filigree cross copied from a famous balcony iron work of the Vieux Carré in New Orleans. In the center of the cross is placed a diamond pin used intact.

The reverse of the *gloria* is made up of a rich grape design entirely of gold, bearing between the scrolls large shields with the coats of arms of the nine Archbishops of New Orleans. Between them are two scrolls and seven shields showing the arms and dates of the episcopal administrations and Auxiliary Bishops of the See. These scrolls carry the dates of the administrations of the Bishops of Quebec and those of the Spanish period.

At the front of the monstrance, near the point of the junction of the *shaft* with the *gloria,* is found a silver statuette of Our Lady of Prompt Succor, patroness of the City of New Orleans. The figure is a replica of the famous statue at the Ursuline Convent in New Orleans.

At the base of the *shaft* stand five silver statuettes— St. Louis, King of France; patron of the Archdiocese of New Orleans, patron of the Cathedral; St. Francis of Assisi, recalling the pioneer Capuchin missionaries in New Orleans; St. Ignatius Loyola, recalling the Jesuit missionaries in Louisiana; St. Francis de Sales, symbolizing the pioneer secular clergy; and St. Vincent de Paul, secondary patron of the Archdiocese and symbolic of the first Vincentian missionaries in Louisiana. Finally, at the *base,* are five large medallions in colored enamel bearing the coats of arms of Pope Pius XI, reigning Pope during the Congress; Pope Pius VI, who erected the Diocese of New Orleans in 1793; the Great Seal of the United States, that of the State of Louisiana, and the Seal of the City of New Orleans. Set in between the large medallions are five smaller ones bearing the coats of arms of the five civil governments under which the Church of Louisiana served—France, Spain, the Confederacy, the United States of America; the fifth has the coat of arms of the Archdiocese of New Orleans. Above this Archdiocesan shield is a crescent-shaped, diamond-studded broach used intact, representing the Crescent City of New Orleans.

Near the edge of the *base* is a circle of 26 shields, carrying the coats of arms of the Archdioceses and Dioceses that have been carved out of the original Diocese of New Orleans since the Louisiana Purchase.

The entire Monstrance rests on 10 designed gold legs or claws. It weighs 25 pounds and is entirely handmade of 14 carat gold, with the exception of the statuettes and angels and the precious jewels.

The monstrance was first used for the Benediction of the Blessed Sacrament on Tuesday the 18th of October, 1938.

R.B.

31) PECTORAL CROSS; Italy, 20th century (before ca. 1977); gold, pearls and emeralds; height 6¾", width 4⁵⁄₁₆", thickness ½". *Sacristy, Sistine Chapel,* Vatican City

Signed "Del Vecchio," the cross contains a relic of *Saint Raffaella Maria Porros Ayllon,* foundress of the Congregation of the Handmaidens of the Holy Cross. Offered to His Holiness Paul VI by the sisters of the Congregation on the occasion of the solemn ceremony of canonization of the saint, held in the Basilica of St. Peter, January 23, 1977.

G.M.

32) FRANÇOIS RANVOYZÉ; 1739–1819; **CIBORIUM, CHALICE AND MONSTRANCE;** signed and dated 1810, n.d., 1812; gold. *Musée du Québec*, Quebec City, Canada

This ensemble of a ciborium, chalice and monstrance forms the focus of the Treasury of the Musée du Québec's early French-Canadian goldsmith work. The gold ciborium is a signed work, dated 1810, with a height of 24,5 cm. The gold chalice is signed but not dated and is 24,7 cm high. The gold monstrance is signed and dated 1812 with a height of 39 cm. These three works constitute the high point of François Ranvoyzé's creative productivity. Fortunately, they have survived and are on loan by special agreement of the Archdiocese of Québec and the Musée du Québec.

V.A.Mc.

33) THE TAPESTRY OF ST. JOAN OF ARC ARRIVING AT THE CHATEAU DE CHINON; 1430; wool; height 31½″, width 41¼″. *Musée Historique Orléans*, France

This remarkable small tapestry was made a few years after the death of St. Joan of Arc and is the earliest known reproduction of her. It is the treasure of the *Centre Jeanne d'Arc*, and is on loan to the Vatican Pavilion by special agreement. St. Joan, along with St. Louis, King of France, are popular saints in the Archdiocese of New Orleans, reflecting the French heritage.

V.A.Mc.

34) THE NURSING MADONNA; France, early 15th century, c. 1400; limestone; height 40½″, width 17¾″. *Louvre*, Paris, France

In early Christian iconography, the representation of the Virgin and the child centered on the portrayal of the divinity of Jesus, and with Mary the mother of God. This artistic genre strove to reveal the majesty of God in Jesus Christ. Beginning with the 13th century, and extending into the 14th and 15th centuries, a dramatic change in emphasis took place. Mary was depicted more as a tender mother, and Jesus as a young, lovable baby. This significant change occurred directly as the result of the new Christian humanism of St. Francis of Assisi and the Franciscan cult of the Sacred *Bambino*, as found in the innovative idea of the crib, or creche. Tenderness appears in artistic representations—so much so that we see Mary as a beautiful and delicate young mother. Thus, the qualities of glory and transcendence gave way to the pride and delight of a young mother in her baby.

By the beginning of the 1400s, and especially in this exquisite *Nursing Madonna*, Mary had become a young queen, with her infant son nursing at her breast. A touch of affected graciousness is reflected in the pose of the virgin, especially in her right hand, which reveals the courtly life of the day. The model may have been Blanche of Castille, the mother of St. Louis; she radiates joy and queenly grace.

The first known portrayal of Mary crowned appeared in the city of Senlins, northeast of Paris, which belonged to the crown. At first, the tradition showed Mary crowned by her son; later, it simply showed the madonna crowned. The cult of the virgin-queen exalted the place and respect for women, and the importance of motherhood. The earliest known rendering of the virgin nursing her son is from Pisa, toward the end of the 12th century and the beginning of the 13th. The transition from the stress on the glory of God, so common in the Byzantine and Romanesque periods, then gave way to the loving humanity of Jesus Christ and his charming mother in this Nursing Madonna.

R.P.

35) THE CHAMPAGNE MADONNA AND CHILD;

France, 16th century, c. 1510; Polychromed sandstone; height 37¼″, width 17¾″. *Musée National des Thermes et de l'Hôtel de Cluny, Paris, France*

By the 16th century, the humanity of the Christ Child was so well established that the artist portrayed him as an almost nude child in his mother's arms, playing with a bird. Typical of the sculpture of the Champagne countryside, Mary is depicted as a wealthy, serenely happy mother, almost totally preoccupied with her son. The richly gathered drapery of the dress, with many precious details, reflects the successful background of the Champagne landowner class, which undoubtedly commissioned this significant sculpture. Many of the prosperous Champagne families commissioned religious statues which depicted at once the faith and wealth of the region, and especially the devotion to Mary as the mother of their countryside, and of all of those who dwelt in the land.

The face of the virgin, with its high forehead, long Botticelli-like hair, and peaceful countenance creates an impression of deep love and devotion. It was originally a richly polychromed sandstone sculpture. Only traces of the polychrome remain. The contrast between the rich texture of the sculptured dress and the simplicity of the treatment of the madonna's head and the child's body, contribute much to the artistic beauty of the piece.

It was bought in 1905 for the Musée de Cluny from a private antiquarian.

R.P.

36) THE ANNUNCIATION; Constantinople, 8th-early 9th century; silk-compound twill; height 13¼″, width 27″. *Biblioteca Apostolica Vaticana, Museo Sacro, Vatican City*

The Annunciation to Mary appears twice, in repeat pattern, within beautifully designed medallions on this

45

very fine and rare fragment of silk. The archangel Gabriel approaches the Virgin, who sits on a jeweled throne flanked by baskets for the wool with which she was believed to have woven the veil of the temple in Jerusalem. The fabric lined the rectangular silver reliquary for the sandals of Christ, one of the most precious relics of the *Sancta Sanctorum* at the Lateran in Rome, where the reliquary is recorded as early as the mid-ninth century.

The Annunciation, like a similar silk fragment depicting the Nativity, also from the *Sancta Sanctorum*, was probably cut from fabric imported from Constantinople and used for one of the hundreds of curtains that were given to Roman churches by the popes dur-

ing the eighth and ninth centuries, as recorded in the *Liber Pontificalis*. One of these curtains, with a medallion of the Nativity comparable in size to that of *The Annunciation* silk, was illustrated in the frescoes that Pope John VII (705-7) had painted in the church of *Santa Maria Antica* in the Roman Forum.

The richness and complexity of the design and coloration of *The Annunciation* place it in the forefront of a group of highly prized decorative silks, many with secular subjects, that survive because they were used in Western medieval churches to wrap relics.

M.E.F.

37) THE CRUCIFIXION; The Romans French Embroidered Tapestry; mid-16th century; wool and silk embroidered on linen; height 141⅝", width 110¼". *Église Collegiale St. Bernard,* Romans, France

Four tapestries out of a series of 15, dealing with Jesus' public ministry, executed from the same sketches as the tapestries on the Passion in the Cathedral of Angers, once thought to be the work of Van Room of Brussels, but this is now contested. The date 1555 is indicated on the Resurrection panel.

In the 17th Century, this series belonged to Helène Tardif, daughter of a drapery merchant of Romans. She was the widow of Peter Deloulle, consistorial lawyer in

the parliament of Grenoble. His coat of arms, blue with three silver doves on top sewn with gules, endowed with a pendant cross of gold held by the same, had been worked for the panel of the Crucifixion. In 1677, Helène Tardif willed the collection to the Ursuline monastery at Romans. Later acquired by Charles de Lionne-Lesseing, chaplain of the chapter of St. Bernard, the tapestries were divided into two lots at his death in 1701. Seven pieces were sold in Paris at public auction in 1705; the remaining eight were allotted to the chapter of St. Bernard, the legatee.

T.F.

GALLERY FOUR

GEORGES ROUAULT, ECCE HOMO

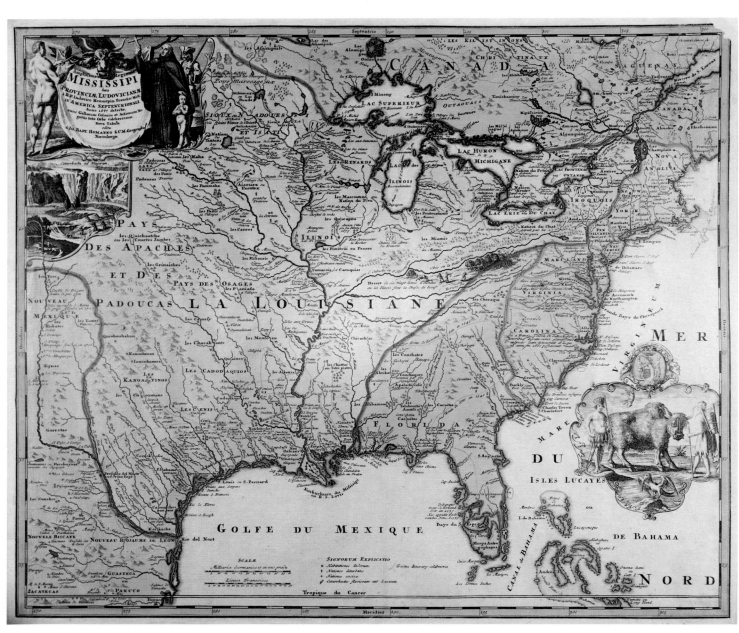

Map 4—La Louisiane
The Homann Map of 1687, 19″ × 22″
(The Macdonald-Stewart Foundation)

GALLERY FOUR

"To those who receive the Spirit, the water of the Spirit turns into a spring welling up unto eternal life" (John 4:14).

38) SALVADOR DALI; 1904; **MADONNA OF PORT LLIGAT;** 1949; oil on canvas; height 19½", width 15¹⁄₁₆". *Marquette University Museum of Art*, Milwaukee, Wisconsin. Gift of Mr. and Mrs. Ira Haupt.

Salvador Dali painted *The Madonna of Port Lligat* (1949) in his beloved Port Lligat, a tiny fishing village on the Spanish coast between Barcelona and the French border, shortly after he returned from the United States, where he had lived during World War II. A preliminary sketch, called a "Study for the Ma-

donna of Port Lligat" (1949), is in a private collection. A larger painting, with notable differences in the rendition of the subject and expansion of the symbolism, is presently in the collection of Lady Beaverbrook of New Brunswick, Canada.

Dali traveled to Rome with this smaller *Madonna of Port Lligat* during 1949, when he met with Pope Pius XII. The Pope showed great interest in Dali's surrealist interpretation of the Madonna and Child theme. In the spirit of a Holy Year, the Pope accepted the sincerity of Dali's pilgrimage and blessed the work. Acquired by Mr. and Mrs. Ira Haupt of New York, it remained in their home until 1959, when they presented it to Marquette University.

The 1949 *Madonna of Port Lligat* marks several important transitions in Dali's career: a gradual break with the Surrealists with whom he had been identified for many years, a public identification with Catholicism symbolized by his visit to Pius XII, and the beginning of a series of important religious works that he was to produce over the next several years. In these works, and especially here, Dali combines a tradition of classical Western painting with Surrealism.

Dali was influenced by classical painters, notably by Piero della Francesca and Raphael. Dali himself refers to Piero's *The Virgin and Child with Saints and Angels* (*Pinacoteca Di Brera*, Milan) as the inspiration for his *Madonna of Port Lligat*. Similarities exist between Dali's *Madonna of Port Lligat* (1949) and the Brera Madonna. Both Madonnas are seated on thrones with their hands clasped together and forming an arch above the Christ Child. Both are prominently centered under an arch beneath which a white egg hangs by a string from a large sea shell. Even a casual survey of Raphael's Madonnas will show that Dali's *Madonna of Port Lligat* (1949) belongs to the same tradition. Raphael's *Madonna Di Foligno*, now located in the Vatican Museum *Pinacoteca*, also shows the Madonna and Child suspended in space above the earth. A comparison of the paintings affirms Dali's substantial debt to Raphael.

Within an artistic framework representing the conjunction of classical and surrealist styles, Dali manifests a religious mysticism which can be traced to the Spaniards, St. John of the Cross and St. Teresa of Avila.

Dali's use of the concept of "dematerialization" illustrates the impact the atomic age had made upon him. He explains his meaning: the changes in matter resulting from an atomic explosion are parallel to his spiritual transformation of the Madonna. Because of her unique role, her physical body is "dematerialized." The open space cut through her torso, for instance, becomes a "mystical and virginal tabernacle" where the Christ Child resides. Her mask-like face and head are suspended above dismembered hands and arms. The Christ Child "floats" inside the tabernacle space.

Dali's allusions to the atomic age, combined with his use of surrealist imagery, show his intention to produce a modern painting, not a mere working of a familiar theme according to an earlier style. The modernity of the *Port Lligat Madonna* is also suggested in his use of modern optics. A remarkable sense of spatial depth is achieved here by introducing three-dimensional stereoscopic qualities. The colors of striking clarity suggest the medium of modern color photography, which may have influenced Dali's approach to the painting.

Although the principal symbolism centers on the Madonna and Child, Dali's use of that theme is more complex than at first appears. On one level, the *Port Lligat Madonna* is the mystical symbol of Christianity, as she is in the paintings of Piero della Francesca and of Raphael. With quiet dignity, she exemplifies the spiritual values associated historically with the Madonna. As the first religious work that Dali created, the *Port Lligat Madonna* also represents Dali's own synthesis of these values into an image suitable for the modern world.

The *Port Lligat Madonna* is also intended as homage to his wife, Gala, who was the model for his painting. "Gala, my wife, whom I had the miraculous good fortune to choose, is a unique person whose image is comparable to the serene perfections of the Renaissance. In all the genre paintings, therefore, there is the one and only presence of that visible woman, Gala, my wife." For Dali, Gala was both Helen of Troy and Madonna, the sensuous and spiritual ideals in one, the guiding force in his life.

The *Madonna of Port Lligat* is thus to be doubly understood, first as the Madonna of the mystical spirit, and then as Dali's tribute to his beloved wife. Dali's "humanized" Gala-Madonna is actually more prominently emphasized, however, in the 1950 version of the *Port Lligat Madonna*, whose strongly realistic figures are closer to modern photo-realism than to Renaissance models.

Although in a visually subordinate role, the Christ Child has a central place in the meaning of this painting. Dali's model for the Child is Juan Figueras, a fisherman's son from Cadaques. The symbolism here, as with the egg, the inverted shell and the fish, appears to rely upon conventional meanings. Christ's domination over the earth is indicated by his placement in the tabernacle that has replaced the Madonna's torso, and by the world and cross that surround him.

The egg and the sea shell trace back to Piero della Francesca's Brera Altar in Milan, as noted earlier, except that Dali inverts the sea shell. In a Renaissance painting, an egg often symbolized the resurrection, sometimes (as in the work of Piero della Francesca) the four elements of the earth. Dali discusses the importance of the egg at length in his book, *Fifty Secrets of Magic Craftsmanship*. He compares it to a world suspended from heaven. In this painting, the egg represents the unity of the Catholic Church in the world. Its placement over the Madonna signals her prominence in that world sphere. Or, as we have said, the egg may additionally represent the central roles of Gala, and of painting, in the artist's personal world.

Sea shells, in particular scallop shells, may represent pilgrimage or baptism. The fish, according to the conventions of Christian tradition, represents Christ. The lemons are associated with fidelity in love.

The sea urchin, especially prominent in this painting, has a unique meaning for Dali. He invites one to view his painting through the microscopic world of a sea urchin's skeleton fitted with a crystal lens. He uses this device to measure the perfection of his paintings. He also compares the "architectural" structure of the skeleton of a sea urchin to the finest of man-made architectural structures, and likens the sea urchin's role in the life of a painter to the role of a human skeleton in the life of a saint. The saint who periodically knows ecstasies and is drawn by "other-worldly" concerns, is reminded of his earthly condition by a human skull. The painter, whose ecstasies are primarily related to the material world, requires the skeleton of the sea urchin to remind him of the celestial regions beyond the sensuality of his oils.

Especially important to a complete reading of this painting is the role played by architecture. Dali follows the Renaissance painters, particularly Piero della Francesca, in his use of the architecture surrounding the Madonna and Child. From the Middle Ages on, architecture has been used to express essential thoughts. In the later Renaissance, the principal figures in a painting are frequently enclosed in an architectural structure (Piero's Brera Altar). The architecture is intended to express a synthesis of humankind and the world, and is the point of view through which the painter perceives the people and nature itself. In this instance, Dali shows the human figures suspended in space, fragmented, and dismembered; what he is saying, then, is that they are mystically transcendent in respect to the world.

The *Madonna of Port Lligat* painting joins together the prophet's words, "Behold, a Virgin shall conceive a Son!" and the pendulum of atomic force that keeps "clocking over time and space."

C.L.C.

39) GEORGES ROUAULT; 1871–1958; **JEANNE d'ARC;** 1948–1949; oil on wood; height 23⅞″, width 18⅞″. Private collection

One of Rouault's favorite subjects was the Patroness of France, St. Joan of Arc. In this rendering she is shown astride her horse with the sun of glory shining upon her. It shows, like other Rouaults, the strong influence of his stained-glass period, which gives solidity, design, and form to his work. Better than other contemporary French artists, Rouault reveals his passion for the spiritual, and desire to pierce through the surface of things so as to reveal the internal reality of man's salvation. Rouault found in St. Joan the unique combination of the mystical life wedded to an active apostolate.

V.A.Mc.

40) GEORGES ROUAULT; 1871–1958; **ECCE HOMO;** 1952; oil on wood; height 31½″, width 29⅛″; signed in lower right hand corner. *The Vatican Museums—Collection of Modern Religious Art*, Vatican City

At an early age Rouault was introduced to the great masters like Rembrandt, Daumier, and Courbet. By 1885, he was apprenticed in the Hirsch Studio of Stained Glass Restoration. He entered the Ecole des Beaux-Arts in 1890 as a pupil of Gustave Moreau. Among his fellow-students were Matisse, Marquet, Lehmann and Manguin, who later formed the Les Fauves Group. He fell under the influence of Léon Bloy and was inspired by his Christian social consciousness. As a result, he created a series of deeply moving "Christs" under the aspect of his passion. Rouault frequently used the face of Christ for the subject of his paintings. He was deeply moved by the suffering which occurred as a result of the two great wars. His principal themes were Christian compassion, human pathos, fallibility and hypocrisy, symbolized in clowns, prostitutes and judges; but most of all, the biblical themes. The suffering of Christ, and later the Christ of the Galilean years became the recurring themes of his works.

This example depicting the moment when Christ is brought forth by Pilate who proclaimed, "Behold the man," is executed with the fullness of his maturity and concludes the French artist's pictorial evolution. The depth of his Christian sentiment led him to see in the theme of the passion of Christ, a symbol of all humanity's suffering. Jesus' suffering was for Rouault the matrix of his profound understanding of suffering and death.

M.F.

41) RAPHAEL; 1483–1520; **JESUS ON THE CROSS WITH MARY AND JOHN;** Made from a Raphael drawing by the St. Michael Studio in Rome, 1724; tapestry in wool and silk; height 150⅞″, width 40⅛″. *Lateran Palace*, Rome, Italy

Like Michelangelo, Raphael was one of a group of artists invited to Rome by Pope Julius II to embellish the rooms on the third floor of the Vatican Palace. With the accession of Pope Leo X (1513), Raphael was commissioned to design tapestries for the Sistine Chapel.

Shortly thereafter, he drew a working-sketch for a crucifixion scene to be hung above the altar in the Sistine Chapel. It was started in 1724 by the Studio of St. Michael, in Rome; Raphael's sketch was carried out to the last detail. Like his painting, *The Crucified Christ with Saints*, the tapestry treats of one of Raphael's favorite themes, that is, the moment of Jesus' death. At that moment, on Calvary, Jesus entrusted His mother to the care of the Apostle John, saying, "Woman, behold your son," and (to John), "Son, behold your mother" (John 19:26).

The tapestry, which has been carefully restored for the Vatican Pavilion Exhibition, is a marvelous example of Raphael's genius. The design is powerful, the execution faultless. Mary stands at the foot of the cross, wrapped in sorrow. John strains to hear the words of Jesus. The cross stands on Golgotha, the little hill (the Skull) on which Christ was crucified outside the walls of Jerusalem. The Holy City can be seen in the background. The overall effect is most impressive.

At the bottom of the tapestry, the coat of arms of Pope Clement XII appears. The tapestry is now housed in the *Lateran Palace* in Rome.

V.A.Mc.

42) ST. JOHN THE BAPTIST IN THE WILDERNESS; Cantarini School; 17th century; oil on canvas; restored 1971; height 49⅛″, width 38¼″. *National Gallery of Ireland*, Dublin, Ireland

St. John the Baptist went into the wilderness to prepare himself through a life of self-denial for his public ministry as the Precursor of Jesus Christ—the one who would announce the imminent coming of the Lamb of God. Here, he is portrayed in a paradoxical position; partly in contemplative repose, and yet hand raised dramatically as the preacher of the coming of the Lamb of God. In John's Gospel, it says, "The next day John saw Jesus coming towards him, and he said, 'Behold the Lamb of God, who takes away the sin of the world!' " (John 1:29). The pose symbolizes the contemplative source of his preaching ministry. The lamb is used in this painting as the artistic allusion to the text.

The character and style of this painting is certainly in the tradition of the Guido Reni School. Such authorities as Denis Mahon and Stephen Pepper firmly ascribe the name of Simone Cantarini to this painting. Following its acquisition, the painting was catalogued as by Guercino down to and including the 1898 catalogue of the National Gallery of Ireland. Then, it was dropped until it was ascribed to Reni in the 1963 catalogue, and to Cantarini in both the 1971 and 1981 editions.

Reportedly it is from the collection of the Marchese Campana of Rome.

M.W.

43) GUIDO RENI; 1575–1642; **ST. JOSEPH WITH THE CHRIST CHILD;** c. 1625; oil on canvas; height 28″, width 20″. Private Collection

This exquisite Guido Reni shows the popular contrast between the aged St. Joseph and the beauty of the innocent Christ Child. The coloration and mood reflect the profound awe of Joseph in caring for Jesus. Its tenderness, restraint, and yet spontaneous rendering reflect the delight of the two in one another. The fruit which Jesus holds may be an orange, or a pomegranate, possibly expressing the fruitfulness of redemption which will come forth from this Child.

V.A.Mc.

44) THE SPEAR-CROSS; France, 19th century; (before 1877); gilded silver, gold, enamel and precious stones; height 104⅜″, width 16″. *Sacristy, Sistine Chapel,* Vatican City

Christ the King appears on the front, wearing a crown of gold and enamel studded with rubies and emeralds. His robe is of green gold, with a sash embroidered in white and green enamel. On the back, the Virgin stands with outstretched arms. Her robe of gold sequins is adorned with white and blue lines, with delicate white leaves in the veil and on her gown. The haloes of both Christ and Mary are speckled with green and white and adorned with pearls, emeralds, and rubies. Six seraphim, with wings of enameled blue in many hues and sparkling with sapphires, are posted at either end of the cross, and on both sides. Adam and Eve kneel at the foot of the cross on corbels of palm branches col-

ored in green. Beneath them is the earthly globe in which the five continents and an angel bearing the Gospel appear. Twelve large enameled roses cover the poles of the sphere, and the signs of the zodiac cut diagonally across the globe upon a band of red gold embroidered with stars. Farther down, the biblical serpent in enamel of green gold twines around the handle on the lower portion of which is Leo XIII's coat of arms.

The shaft of the cross is adorned with flowers (mysotis) in natural color and with vine branches which stretch out their branches on the arms of the cross.

The dedicatory inscription, with sapphire bosses spacing it, runs along the shaft and reads:
Given, on the happy occasion of the 50th anniversary of his ordination to the priesthood, to the Most Holy Father Leo XIII, PONTIFEX MAXIMUS, by the Diocese of Moulins (France), on December 31, 1888.

G.M.

45) ORAZIO DE' FERRARI; 1606–1657; **THE INCREDULITY OF ST. THOMAS;** 1640; oil on canvas; restored 1980–81; height 64⅞″, width 50⅜″. *National Gallery of Ireland*, Dublin, Ireland

The apostle Thomas was not with the others when the risen Christ appeared to the disciples. Thomas did not believe their story and declared that he would first have to verify the holes in Jesus' hands and feet, and place his hand in the wound in His side, before he would believe (John 20:24 +). Shortly after this (eight days later), Christ again appeared to the disciples; this time Thomas was present. Seeing the Master there, he fell on his knees, exclaiming: "My Lord and my God." The "doubting Thomas" was now the believing Thomas. Jesus invited him then to put his hand into the wounds he bore. It is this moment that de' Ferrari has captured on canvas. The figure to the right-middle is quite surely St. John, at whose side is St. Peter. The head emerging from the background cannot be identified.

The attribution of this picture to de' Ferrari, first proposed by Sergio Benedetti, is plausible, even highly probable, according to Mary Newcombe Schleier. The face of Christ here is similar to one in his *Ecce Homo* (now in a private collection at Genoa). In this, too, is a second prominent figure, not unlike that of St. Thomas. In both paintings the modeling is similar, and a barely discernible figure emerges from a dark background.

A date in or around 1640 is suggested; the *chiaroscuro* is more subdued than it was to become in later works.

M.W.

46) GEORGES DE LA TOUR; 1590–1652; **THE CARPENTER AND THE CHRIST CHILD;** c. 1630; height 54″, width 39¾″. *Louvre*, Paris, France. Gift of Percy Moore Turner.

Discovered in England by Percy Moore Turner, c. 1938, and given by him to the Louvre Museum in memory of Paul Jamot in 1948. Unanimously accepted as a certain and major de la Tour, despite the lack of signature. The freedom of the realism, the care to balance the density of volumes, the decisiveness and fullness of the touch (which the fine radiographic copy confirms), the "plum" tonality where a large area of red does not "take over" clearly bespeak the master's touch. The beginning of his 40th year seems to fit in well with the principal datings proposed up to the present (by Pariset, and Sterling). The painting unites, as many religious texts of the time do, a devotion to Joseph, to the Infant Jesus, and to the cross, which is brought to mind directly by the beam on which the carpenter is working.

This painting has always been accepted as one of de la Tour's major works. Its authenticity has never been doubted. Here, de la Tour once again takes up a caravanesque theme which contrasts the old man and the infant. His composition has been well copied by the author of the Bob Jones University painting (author not certain), and by Trophime Bigot in the collection Boyer d'Aiguilles.

The subject corresponds, not only to the taste of the caravanesques for the scenes of family life, but to the extraordinary development of cult of St. Joseph, especially propagated in the 1600's by the Franciscans and the growing devotion to the Infant Jesus.

With Caravaggio, the possibilities of dramatic lighting began. His influence spread into France, where Georges de la Tour developed it in his own unique style. The source of light is now introduced into the picture, giving a definite focus to the composition. In turn, an outline of forms and volumes emerges, with the broad pattern of light against dark layers of purple, grayish green, and touches of vermilion, all emanating from the brilliant candlelight source.

A second look at this deceptively simple composition reveals the deeper and more mystical aspects of the work. Jesus is holding the light and is protecting it so that Joseph might do his work. A delicately youthful profile of the Christ Child reflects the light, and yet, at the same time, in a mysterious way, is the source of the light. The face of the carpenter has a momentary, almost fleeting, sense of anxiety as he watches over the Child and protects him. The aesthetic sense of the play of lights and darks is wedded to a spiritual sensitivity profoundly moving in its simplicity. The moment of mutual concern is well caught in the painting, and produces a hauntingly beautiful composition of light enveloping the darkness with an overwhelming feeling of peace and serenity.

The painting contrasts dramatically with the personal life of Georges de la Tour. Like Caravaggio himself, he was tormented by many personal problems, although de la Tour was a wealthy land owner. This masterpiece is perhaps his most profoundly simple, and yet strongest, composition of all of his works. This magnificent painting is on loan by special permission of the Government of France and the Louvre.

P.R.

---

47) EL GRECO; 1541–1614; **ST. JOSEPH WITH THE CHRIST CHILD;** 1590–1600; oil on canvas; height 39¾", width 21¼" (52" × 31¼" with frame). *Cathedral of Toledo,* Toledo, Spain

This painting shows St. Joseph and the Christ Child with the City of Toledo in the background. The figures are in the mystical style of El Greco, with angels of the Lord hovering above, celebrating the mystery of God becoming Man. St. Joseph is the special patron of the Universal Church since he protected Christ from his childhood on. The painting is owned by the Cathedral of Toledo and is now on loan to the New Orleans Vatican Pavilion for this exhibition. It was painted

between 1590 and 1600 and is very similar to the one in the Chapel of San José, also in Toledo. The painting was donated to the Parish Chapel of St. Peter, in the Cathedral, by Don Fernando de Elejalde, between 1781 and 1805. It is in good condition.

V.A.Mc.

---

48) EL GRECO; 1541–1614; **THE SAVIOR;** 1590–1600; oil on canvas; height 38¼", width 30½" (46⅞" × 37¾" with frame). *Cathedral of Toledo,* Toledo, Spain

El Greco was born in the year 1541 at Phodele, near Candia in Crete. He was named Domenikos Theotocopoulos but became known simply as El Greco, The

Greek. By 1560, El Greco was in Venice where he became acquainted with Titian, Tintoretto, and other well-known artists of his day. Most likely he worked for a time in Titian's atelier. By 1570, El Greco left Venice and went to Rome where he was received by the miniature painter, Giulio Clovio, and was lodged in the Farnese Palace. During his sojourn in Rome, he painted a number of works which have become famous, especially the *Purification in the Temple,* and the *Victory of Lepanto.* By 1573, El Greco arrived in Spain to live in Madrid for a few years, and then by 1576, he moved to Toledo, where he settled and made his home for the rest of his life.

It was in Toledo that he began the monumental work which reflected the spirit of Spanish mysticism. He took up living quarters in the heart of the Jewish district of the city in the old palace belonging to Samuel Levi, the well-known silversmith of that day. All of his models and sitters were drawn from the Jewish quarter. Much of El Greco's work reflects the ancient civilization from which he came, namely, the Byzantine art which so profoundly influenced his early career. Jewish and Christian subjects of Holy Scripture suitable to describe the divine and human drama became the common subject of his painting, but wrapped in mystery, for they emanated from a source of unknown divine power. In the Byzantine tradition, there is the absence of any action or drama in the portrayal of the subject. It is, rather, a transcendent, static, styl-

ized design, alive with colors, clashing and combining with one another. The ritual character of the compositions, the harmony of colors achieved without the intervention of external light, are elements which El Greco borrowed from the Byzantine tradition and assimilated through his experience with Titian.

El Greco added the dimensions of dramatic light and composition, moving in a live, dynamic fashion, protraying the reality of the subject. He realized the value of the individual brush stroke, but he now transformed Titian's adherence to material portrayal and assimilated it into the mystical tradition of the Spanish ethos, aiming rather to exalt the spiritual existence hidden behind the physical realities which meet the eye. The transcendence and abstraction of the Byzantine tradition prepared him well for the Spanish mysticism into which he moved. His style evolved over a long period of time, an inner fight which Lionello Venturi described as "conquering his antinomies."

El Greco's genius and personality seemed to blossom once he arrived in Toledo. It is from this period of his life that the great masterpieces began to flow from his creative consciousness. His paintings are unique in that they combine a quality of transcendence, Byzantine splendor, and dynamic force through color and light emanating from within the very essence of the painting. The one quality which most markedly distinguishes him from any other artist is the characteristic of his elongations. A seeming unrelated concern with realism of form, combined with a sense of other-worldliness, creates a state of extreme fluidity and ghostlike bodies which do not belong to this world. He consistently alters the organic forms of his bodies by elongation of the figures and by a seeming disregard for nature.

His principal concern, however, was with light and color, a special light found only in his paintings, reflecting his attitude that the actual daylight "disturbs my inner light." His daylight is not the daylight of a Caravaggio, which is always the same no matter how beautiful; his light is a light which at times bursts forth into a flame of color and rhythmical composition, highlighted with greens fading into yellow, and pink into vermilion, and at times extending into complete darkness silhouetted into white. When compared to the subdued, warm, natural colors of a Caravaggio, El Greco's paintings almost appear brittle, agitated and glaring. The light of his paintings almost has nothing in common with daylight. It represents a type of "supernatural explosion of color," as René Huyghe describes it. El Greco opens our eyes to the light of his own creative imagination and creates new light, a kind of transfigured light, based upon the experiences of the inner spirit. It has been described as "a kind of spiritual experience emanating from the eye of the faith-filled soul of El Greco."

It is in this tradition of mystical faith that we view the three works which we have on loan in this New Orleans Vatican Pavilion Exhibition. His personal identity with Christ reveals a profoundly faith-inspired interpretation as can be experienced in *The Savior, Christ on the Cross* and *St. Joseph with the Christ Child.* He embodies Spanish mysticism better than any native Spanish artist.

This celebrated painting by El Greco depicts Jesus Christ as the Savior of the World. He is seated in glory bestowing His blessing. The painting belongs to one of several series of the Apostles and Christ and is perhaps the best one of the series. The whole collection was commissioned by the Cathedral to be displayed in the main Sacristy. The Cathedral is still in possession of the documents concerning the commission, its value and the payment to the artist. It seems that the painting was not finished. It is in good condition.

V.A.Mc.

49) EL GRECO; 1541–1614; CHRIST ON THE CROSS;
date unknown; oil on canvas; height 41¾, width 27¼″; signed at the foot of the cross: . . . kos Theo. . . . (mostly obliterated). *The Ringling Museum,* Sarasota, Florida

Unlike other crucifixions, El Greco tried to capture the mystery of the suffering of Jesus Christ at the climactic moment in which the world is crucified to the cross in Christ. He captures in the somber tones of deep sorrow and pathos the mood of the whole of the earth as it cries out and is touched by the drama of Christ dying for sinful men.

V.A.Mc.

---

50) CARAVAGGIO (MICHELANGELO MERISI); Bergamo 1573—Port' Ercole 1610; **THE DEPOSITION;** 1604; oil on canvas; height 118⅛″, width 79¹³⁄₁₆″. *The Vatican Museums— Painting Galleries,* Vatican City

Certainly, the high point of the New Orleans Vatican Pavilion collection is Caravaggio's famous painting of *The Deposition.* It was originally designed to hang above the main altar of the *Chiesa Nuova* (Santa Maria in Vallicella) in Rome. It was commissioned for the chapel of the Vittrici family, probably towards the end of 1601, and was finished by September of 1604. The painting remained in the Vittrici chapel until 1797, when it was sent to Paris according to the terms of the Treaty of Tolentino of 1797.

Michelangelo Caravaggio was the most original and daring painter of his time. Born in Milan in 1573, he began his career in Rome, where he quickly became notorious for his wild and violent life.

He developed an extremely dramatic style, thanks to the skillful way he contrasted light and darkness in his painting (*chiaroscuro*).

St. Philip Neri had dedicated the chapels in his new church to the mysteries of the Rosary. The Rosary was in fact somewhat shortened. To the left of the main altar were scenes from the life of the Virgin. As her life was inextricably bound up with that of her son, six altar-pieces were devoted to him, beginning with the Nativity and ending with the Ascension. *The Deposition* was the fifth of these, and represents a daring departure from the traditional style of his day.

Caravaggio's treatment of the subject is not a deposition, in the strict sense, since the Body of Christ is not being lowered into the tomb. Caravaggio represents, instead, the moment when the Body of Christ was placed on the stone of unction. Symbolically, the slab alludes to Christ as the Cornerstone of the Church. The inclusion of the yew beneath the stone possibly recalls a passage in Isaiah (53:2) that refers to Christ, while the fig beside the entrance to the sepulchre is probably the Resurrection symbol of the two parables in Luke (13:6–9; 21:29–31). The presence of the Virgin is due to the necessity of representing the same subject, the Pietà, which appeared in the previous altarpiece of the chapel.

Caravaggio's painting depicts the anguish of the moment, Mary Magdelene, arms extended heavenwards, expresses her intense sorrow. Mary, the mother of Jesus, is painted as an elderly lady expressing her profound compassion. Nicodemus, who is lowering the Body of Christ onto the slab, assisted by John, looks out of the painting at the viewer as if to say, "Behold

him who has given his life for you." John, as he lowers the head and shoulders of Christ onto the slab, inadvertently places his finger into the wound of Christ's side, from which a drop of blood flows. Many authorities have pointed out that this is one of those almost perverse characteristics of Caravaggio's uniqueness as a painter, interpreting anew the ancient incident, but with the twist of his own genius.

The influence of Michelangelo, his namesake, is definitely present in this composition, and, as many critics have pointed out, recalls the Michelangelo *Pietà* in St. Peter's Basilica.

Within six years after Caravaggio had completed *The Deposition*, he was dead. The painting was done when he was thirty-one years of age in 1604. In 1606 he was involved in a murder and fled from Rome, never to return.

This painting of *The Deposition* represents the high point of Caravaggio's genius. While conventional in certain ways, it represents the birth of a new age of painting, initiating the Baroque school of interpretation where emotion is intensely portrayed through contrasts of light and darkness. The picture is one of the few about which there has been almost universal agreement: it is said to be Caravaggio's greatest work.

F.M.

51) HENRY MOORE; **STUDY FOR GIOVANNI BELLINI'S "PIETÀ";** 1975; pencil, chalk, crayon and watercolor; inscribed lower right "Moore '75"; height 16¼", width 12⅝". *Henry Moore Foundation*, Much Hadham, England

Henry Moore is best known as the outstanding contemporary sculptor, but he is also famous as a painter. When, some years ago, the late Franco Russoli, Director of the Pinacoteca Nazionale di Brera, in Milan, invited a number of artists to do interpretative studies of their favorite painting in the Brera, Moore did four studies of Bellini's Pietà. Mary's deep empathy and sorrow at her son's death is strikingly shown as she holds his dead body in her hands.

From this painting, Moore also did two drawings of the hands of Jesus and of Mary.

The painting depicts in contemporary terms what Bellini had in mind, but the style is definitely that of Henry Moore. He graciously loaned this work to the New Orleans Vatican Pavilion. He had intended to do a *Crucifixion* for it, but time and health did not allow him to do so.

V.A.Mc.

GALLERY FIVE

THE GOOD SHEPHERD (detail)

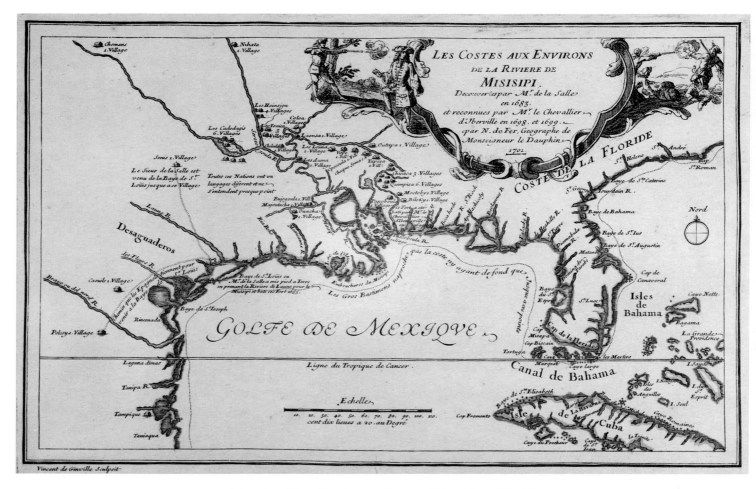

Map 5—The Southern Coast of the New World
The deFer Map of 1701, 9½″ × 14½″
(The Macdonald-Stewart Foundation)

GALLERY FIVE

"Jesus Christ died that we might have everlasting Life" (1 Thess. 5:9–10).

52) DIPTYCH; Central Italy, Rambona, c.A.D. 900; ivory; height 12¼″, total width 10¾″. *Biblioteca Apostolica Vaticana, Museo Sacro*, Vatican City

During the Carolingian era, the format of Late Antique consular diptychs was revived for ecclesiastical purposes. This important example comes from the convent abbey of Rambona (near Ancona).

The left panel is divided into three zones. In the center is the Crucifixion of the living triumphant Christ, between the Virgin—above whose head is the inscription MVLIER EN (His mother)—and St. John, identified by the inscription DISSIPVLE ECCE (Behold the apostle). The cross is surmounted by an oversized double placard inscribed EGO SVM IHS NAZA-RENVS/REX IVDEORVM (I am Jesus of Nazareth/King of the Jews). To the left and right, the Sun and the Moon witness the event, while, at the top, two angels support a medallion portraying God the Father offering a benediction. Below the Crucifixion is the unusual, if not unique, representation of the she-wolf suckling Romulus and Remus, which carries the inscription in Latin, translated as, Romulus and Remus fed by the wolf.

The right panel, likewise, is. organized into three zones. At the top, the enthroned Virgin and Child are positioned between two seraphim, who stand on interlaced circles. Standing below, amidst designs of vine tendrils, are the three patron saints of the abbey of Rambona, and at the bottom is a semiprostrate saint holding palm branches (?). These scenes are accompanied by the quasi-literate inscription in Latin, whose translation reads:

"To the saints Gregory, Silvester, and Flavian, confessors of Christ, for the monastery of Rambona, which Ageltruda built. I, Odelricus, who humbly serve God, had this sculpture made."

C.T.L.

53) PLAQUE FROM A BOOK COVER, WITH A MAIESTAS DOMINI; Italy, Venice or Amalfi; late 11th–early 12th century; ivory; height 9⁹⁄₁₆″, width 5¹⁄₁₆″. *Biblioteca Apostolica Vaticana, Museo Sacro, Vatican City*

This imposing *Maiestas Domini* was originally the central composition of a book cover.

This reconstruction, with Christ enthroned in a mandorla, flanked by a cherub (Cherv/bin) and a seraph (Sera/phin,) and by the Evangelists' symbols, conforms to standard iconography of the Carolingian period in the West. The message inscribed in the open book that Christ holds on his knee, *EG O/SV (M) RE/SVRREC/CIOET/VITA*, or I am the Resurrection and the Life (John 11:25), figures traditionally in Last Judgment iconography. As the Son of God, Christ judges; as the Son of Man, he redeems the sin of Adam and offers resurrection and life by undergoing the Crucifixion. Saints *Gervasius (S(ANCTVS) GER/VASI/VS,)* and *Protasius (P(RO)TA/SI/VS)* appear below Christ in the *Maiestas Domini*; their parents, Saints *Vitalis and Valeria*, are shown below the Crucifixion.

The *Maiestas Domini* plaque is first mentioned in 1756 as being in the Camaldolese monastery on the island of San Michele in the bay of Venice. Since the mid-nineteenth century it has been in the *Biblioteca Apostolica Vaticana*.

D.MacK.E.

54) Probably by NICOLAS MOSTAERT (NICOLÒ PIPPI) OF ARRAS (active 1578–1601/4), after a wax model by Daniele da Volterra (1509–1566), based on drawings attributed to Michelangelo (1475–1564); **THE DESCENT FROM THE CROSS;** Flemish, executed in Rome, c. 1579; ivory, cut out and mounted on a slate plaque, set in an ebony frame inlaid with silver ajouré and engraved ornamental plaquettes and with eight cutout cherubs holding instruments of the Passion; relief: height 11⁷⁄₁₆″, width 8¹⁵⁄₁₆″ (17¹⁵⁄₁₆″ × 14¹⁵⁄₁₆″ with frame). *Biblioteca Apostolica Vaticana, Museo Sacro, Vatican City*

This Vatican relief is based on a well-known composition, the idea for which was attributed, as early as 1610, to Michelangelo.

The Michelangelesque composition has been adapted by Nicolo Pippi with a remarkable feeling for its melodious and emotional impact. A precise, sensitive use of the chisel here results in a noble stylization and a pronounced graphic quality.

The ebony frame does not appear to be contemporary with the relief. The style of the cherubs carrying the instruments of the Passion, and of the ornamental plaquettes, suggests that the frame was made in southern Germany, about 1700.

The ivory was the gift of Gregory XVI (1831–46), who, according to a letter recently discovered by Giovanni Morello in the Vatican Library archives, purchased it in 1835 from a Tommaso Pansieri.

O.R.

MEMORIAL GLASSES

Early Christian art-forms grew out of pagan and Jewish traditions. This transitional art-form is represented in our Vatican Pavilion Exposition by four excellent memorial glasses which were originally drinking glasses and later became memorials attached to tombs.

These four glasses are unique. They have survived from the 3rd and 4th centuries, and they reveal the beliefs and values of those people for whom they were created.

55) BOTTOM OF A DRINKING VESSEL, WITH PORTRAIT BUSTS OF A HUSBAND AND WIFE;
Alexandria, first half of the 3rd century A.D.; glass and gold foil; diameter 4¼". *Biblioteca Apostolica Vaticana, Museo Sacro,* Vatican City

The disk containing the portraits and the inscription is intact; its periphery and part of the rim on the underside—which, originally, formed the foot of the vessel—are fragmentary. There is some discoloration, mostly around the border.

The husband and wife are portrayed frontally before a parapet. She wears a tunic and a pallium knotted at the breast; he is dressed in a tunic and pallium from which his right hand, posed in a gesture of speech, emerges. Just within the band surrounding the portrait, at the top, is a Latin inscription ("Gregory, drink and drink to thine").

This medallion is one of the finest examples of the "brushed technique," in which the shadows producing the modeling are made by a moderately stiff brush. The technique, which was reserved for portraits, is thought to exemplify Alexandrian workmanship, either as practiced in Egypt or by immigrant artists living in Rome.

Most scholars believe that these vessels were used

by the deceased during his lifetime, rather than having been made for funerary purposes. This piece obviously celebrated the marriage or anniversary of the couple. It was found attached to a tile, in the Catacomb of Pamphilius, on May 31, 1926.

K.R.B.

56) JEWISH MEMORIAL GLASS; glass with gold leaf; Rome, 4th century A.D.; diameter 3⁵⁄₁₆″ (4⁵⁄₁₆″ at lip). *Biblioteca Apostolica Vaticana, Museo Sacro,* Vatican City

The Jewish Memorial Glass is a well-ordered design. The Torah-Ark which houses the sacred scrolls is flanked by two lions, recalling the Lion of Judah. Each of the six scrolls (of the Law and the Prophets) has a red dot in the center. Two menorah (7-branched lamp stands) in the lower half of the design are separated by a palm branch, the red flame inclined toward the Ark. A vase supports a festive palm branch (*Lulab*) with red leaves on either side; to the left two ram's horns flank the lamp stand; balancing this on the right is a vase decorated with a red dot and a citron (*Ethrog*). A symbolic jar recalls to the viewer the ceremonial oils (or water) used in Jewish worship. These objects could refer to the festival of *Sukkot* or Booths. The most interesting feature of this memorial glass is its Greek inscription: *Anastasis,* or "resurrection." It will be recalled that the Pharisees believed in the resurrection of the body. The glass shows the rim chipped and cut as a result of separation from the rest of the cup at the time of burial. The front portion is slightly concave; the back slightly convex. A variant reading could be *Anastasi Pie Zeses,* possibly meaning "Anastasius drinks, may he live."

G.M.

57) CHRISTIAN MEMORIAL GLASS; Rome, 4th century A.D.; glass with gold leaf; diameter, 2¾″ (3⅛″ at lip). *Biblioteca Apostolica Vaticana, Museo Sacro,* Vatican City

At the center is Christ with a halo, without beard and with long hair falling in curls to his shoulders, dressed in tunic and pallium. He holds the hem with his left hand while his right hand is placed on his chest in a gesture of speaking. He is shown erect, in a frontal position, on a mountain symbolized by three peaks, a favorite place for divine manifestations. At the sides, also in frontal position, but with their faces turned toward the Risen Christ, one on the right and one on the left, are the Apostles Peter and Paul, both dressed in tunic and pallium. Peter's foot touches the rock, an oblique reference to Jesus' words, "You are Peter (Cephas, or rock) and upon this rock I will build my Church" (Matthew 16:18).

The glass is broken and cut all around, with almost two-thirds of the lip missing. A portion of the gold leaf is slightly peeling from the right arm of the figure of Peter.

Beside the respective figures are the gold inscriptions PETRVS PAVLVS, in capital letters with the S placed in diagonal. Gold is the well-known ancient way of symbolizing immortality and divinity.

According to Garrucci, this piece was the bottom of a cup found intact, still attached to the tomb and stained with the blood of a martyr, by Boldetti in the cemetery of *San Callisto* in Rome and described by him in his works. It was subsequently separated in order to be included in the shrines of the museum which Francesco Vettori was preparing in the Vatican Library under the direction of Benedict XIV (1740–1758). Morey cites a notation from a register of entry of the *Museo Sacro* according to which this piece was donated to Mons. Ratti by Mr. Pollak in 1913.

G.M.

58) CHRISTIAN MEMORIAL GLASS; Rome, 4th century A.D.; glass with gold leaf; diameter 2⅜″ (3⅛″ at lip). *Biblioteca Apostolica Vaticana, Museo Sacro,* Vatican City

The gold of the bottom of the cup has the etched images of the apostles, Peter and Paul, in half bust, in the traditional positions of Peter on the right and Paul on the left, with thick hair and long beards, their faces turned in profile, dressed in tunic and pallium, right hands placed on the chest with folded fingers, indicating the act of speaking, typical in the iconography of the preacher. Between them, in the center toward the top, is the figure of Christ, young with short hair and beardless, dressed in tunic and pallium, who offers with each hand a crown on the head of the two apostles. At the sides of the head of Christ are two globes of gold.

The inscription *PETRVS PAVLVS* is placed, as usual, beside the respective figures. The rim of the glass is broken and cut all around as a result of its separation from the rest of the cup. Slightly concave in the front and convex on the back. The rim of gold which surrounds the scene is lacking in part.

G.M.

A.

B.

59) TWO FRESCO FRAGMENTS; Rome, second half of the 13th century; A. Saint Peter; height 15⅜″, width 10⅞″; B. Saint Paul; height 15″, width 10⅝″. *Reverenda Fabbrica di San Pietro*, Vatican City

These vivid, painted fragments come from a thirteenth-century fresco cycle illustrating the life of Saint Peter that decorated the portico of Old Saint Peter's.

From sketches by Giacomo Grimaldi of the few frescoes that survived from this cycle, made shortly before the portico's destruction in the early seventeenth century, it seems certain that these fragments came from the scene that depicted the episode in which the two apostles to the Romans appeared to the sleeping Emperor Constantine, who, according to legend, was afflicted with leprosy. They instructed him to seek a cure from Pope Silvester I (314–35).

The fragments show only the busts of what were, originally, half-length figures of the apostles standing behind the emperor's bed. The artist exhibits a free and sure hand in his painting, employing broad strokes to form the major folds of the apostles' garments and a finer brush for the heads, which he outlined with a stylus. Since the frescoes were to be seen from some fifty feet below, the top two-thirds of the saints' heads and haloes were raised in relief, to give them extra prominence.

No contemporary documents have survived to record the commissioning of these frescoes or the name of the artist.

M.E.F.

60) EARLY JEWISH INSCRIPTION; Rome, c. 2nd to 3rd century A.D.; white marble; height 9¹⁄₁₆″, width 29½″, depth 1⅜″. *The Vatican Museums—Museo Pio Cristiano, Lapidario Ebraico ex Lateranense*, Vatican City

The gravestone came from the Jewish Catacomb on the *Via Portuense*, on the edge of the present-day *Trastevere* quarter of Rome, outside the *Porta Portese*. The text, in Greek, is enclosed by decorative elements still current in Jewish funerary symbolism: the seven-branched candelabrum, palmette, dove, and flask. The simple inscription reads: ΙΟΥΔΑΣ ΜΗΝΩΝ Ζ ΕΝΘΑΔΕ ΚΕΙΤΕ (Judas, of seven months, lies here). Thus, the gravestone is that of a seven-month-old boy whose name was quite common among the Jewish communities of the Roman Empire. The use of Greek on Jewish gravestones is usual, although inscriptions in Hebrew are not rare either.

I. DiS. M.

Resurrected Christ on the tomb of Paul II in St. Peter's, executed by Dalmata with Mino da Fiesole. The wounds of the passion are displayed in the body of the risen Christ.

O.R.

---

62) GIOTTO (1267?–1337), attributed to; **BUST OF AN ANGEL;** Italy (Tuscany), c. 1310; mosaic; diameter 23¹³/₁₆″. *Reverenda Fabbrica di San Pietro,* Vatican City

This mosaic bust of an angel on a medallion was discovered in 1911 underneath an eighteenth-century copy and was assumed to have belonged to a larger mosaic known as the *Navicella.* This gigantic mosaic was located above the entrance to the atrium of the old Constantinian basilica but is now inside the portico of St. Peter's.

A similar bust, given in 1610 to the church of *San Pietro Ispano* in a small town outside Rome, had an accompanying inscription noting that it had been part of the *Naviculae S. Pietri* (the nave of St. Peter's), and was painted by Iottus (sic) for the atrium of the old Vatican basilica.

The style of the Vatican *Navicella,* in spite of its present condition (the product of extensive restoration in the seventeenth century), and some drawings made shortly before this disfiguration, suggest that a date of about 1310 is very probable for its design. Documents also confirm that Giotto spent time in Rome as late as that year.

However, discrepancies between the Vatican mosaic and the one in *San Pietro Ispano* suggest that different hands worked on what is believed to be Giotto's design. It is unlikely that the painter, himself, participated in the mosaic, as he was not skilled in this type of craftsmanship.

C. G-M.

61) GIOVANNI DALMATA (Ivan Duknovic) (c. 1440–c. 1510); **RELIEF, WITH THE BLESSING CHRIST SEATED IN GLORY;** Rome, c. 1479; marble; height 51½″, width 27⅞″. *Reverenda Fabbrica di San Pietro,* Vatican City

This imposing image of the Redeemer enthroned in heaven was the central panel of the tomb of Cardinal Bernardino Eroli in Old Saint Peter's. Flanking the central image were a relief of Saint Peter and one of Saint Paul, and, below the effigy of the deceased, there were a long inscription and two panels with Eroli's coat of arms. Initially, the tomb was erected in the right transept of the old basilica, but later it was moved to the left nave. It was disassembled in 1606 during the demolition of the nave ordered by Paul V, but most of its sculptural decoration was saved and the single elements reinstalled in various parts of the grottoes beneath Saint Peter's. The present relief is in fairly good condition, except for the broken fingers of Christ's blessing hand, and the transverse arm of the cross.

The solemn vision of this Christ has a direct precedent in the reliefs of God the Father and of the

63) SARCOPHAGUS, WITH RELIEFS OF THE TYPE OF THE PASSION SARCOPHAGI; Rome, c. A. D. 360; marble; height 26⅜", width 81½", depth 30⁵⁄₁₆". *Museo Pio Cristiano*, Vatican City

This sarcophagus, with reliefs only on the front side and lacking its lid, came from the hypogeum of the *Confessio* of *San Paolo fuori le Mura*. It has been in the *Museo Pio Cristiano* since 1854.

The relief frieze is divided into five sections by six olive trees. In the center is the monogram of Christ within a laurel wreath ornamented with gems and ribbons. Below it is a cross, on the arms of which are two doves with outspread wings that pick at the wreath. In the section immediately to the left is Peter, being led away by two soldiers; on the right side is Paul, whose hands have been tied behind his back. A bailiff is drawing his sword. On the far left, Cain and Abel present gifts to God the Father; on the far right is the seated, youthful Job, with his wife and a friend standing in front of him.

The meaning of this sarcophagus relief derives from the symbol of the cross as *crux invicta* (triumphal cross), which occupies the center of the composition, framed by Peter and Paul. The two apostles experience their martyrdoms, but the cross with the laurel wreath, the symbol of victory over death, is before them.

G. D.

The Passion Sarcophagus is another example of early Christian art. It follows the Roman tradition of sculptured marble tombs, and is one of the earliest discovered Christian tombs to depict the story of Jesus' passion. Like most Roman tombs, it is sculpted in high relief, the figures well-proportioned and symmetrically balanced. Such sculptures usually depicted scenes from the life of the deceased, but on this sarcophagus the major events leading to the deaths of Peter and Paul are portrayed. It is thus an expression of the faith of the early Christians. The style is direct and uncompli-

cated. In the triumph of the Cross, portrayed on the central panel, the Christian finds grounds for meaning and hope. The dove, an early Christian symbol, is shown resting upon a very artistic cross, clearly suggesting that Christians find permanent and everlasting rest in the Risen Christ, through the Cross. The dove is likewise a sign of the Holy Spirit, a sign of the Holy Spirit the Christian has received, and a sign of the deceased person whose soul flies to God.

V.A.Mc.

64) THE GOOD SHEPHERD; Rome, late 3rd century; Marble; height: as restored 39⅜", as preserved 21⅝, head 6³⁄₁₆". *Museo Pio Cristiano*, Vatican City

The good shepherd is recognizable as such by his dress. He wears a short, belted garment that leaves his right shoulder bare. On his left side hangs a sheepskin bag that is attached to a long band which extends over his right shoulder. He carries a sheep across his shoulders, holding its feet in both his hands. He has a boyish appearance, with no trace of a beard on his face. Thick locks of hair cover his head and fall over his ears; a few corkscrew curls cascade over his shoulders.

The stylistic singularity of the sculpture lies in the strong contrast between the boy's smooth face and his deeply modeled hair, although one notes the statuette's poor state of preservation, in regard to both the considerable restorations to the face and damage done to the hair. This style—with its unmistakable tendency toward the ornamental—began and developed in the time of the Emperor Gallienus (253–68), shortly after the middle of the third century A.D.

Repeated attempts have been made to relate it to the familiar parables of the "Good Shepherd" in the Scriptures (Matthew 18:12–14; Luke 15:3–7; John 10:11–16), to Paul's Epistle to the Hebrews (13:20), and to the First Epistle of Peter (2:25;5:4). Clement of Alexandria commented on the symbolic aspect of the figure of the shepherd as early as A.D. 200 (*Protrepticus*

provide a mythological background for the shepherd: it was the shepherd, Faustulus, who discovered Romulus and Remus. Under Augustus, bucolic motifs came to symbolize the peace that he had attained, so that the figure of the shepherd assumed an allegorical significance. The portrayal of the Emperor Philip the Arab on the coin commemorating the millennial celebration in A.D. 248 of the founding of Rome has just such a metaphorical meaning. There, a shepherd with seven sheep is pictured as their savior. Toward the close of the third century A.D., when this *Museo Pio Cristiano* youth carrying a sheep was created, non-Christians interpreted the shepherd as a symbol of the *vita felix*, while those familiar with the Scriptures would have recognized in the sculpture an allusion to the "Good Shepherd." The creation of images of shepherds was a tradition that ended—at the latest—in the sixth century A.D.

G.D.

THE GOOD SHEPHERD AND THE LAMB

In Christian iconography the lamb is portrayed as innocent, gentle, and guileless. It puts complete trust in the shepherd, whose voice it knows, and whom it follows in meek obedience. When led to the slaughter, it opens not its mouth, but confidently walks where it is led.

In Old Testament times, God, the Good Shepherd, chose Israel as his beloved land. His people listened to his voice on Mount Sinai and followed him through the desert to the pastures of the Promised Land. Why was it, then, that only the blood of the lamb was able to save Israel and Egypt, and that every morning and evening a lamb had to be offered for the sins of the people (Ex. 29:39)? This was done to indicate that when the sheep had strayed and had gone each his own way, one would come, the true lamb, the true Israel of God, to be stricken for our transgressions (Is. 53). Indeed, God's beloved son descended from heaven and was made the lamb of God. Innocent in his divine splendor, gentle in his human lowliness, guileless as befits the truth, he opened not his mouth when led to the slaughter. On Calvary, our Paschal lamb was sacrificed, yet remained victorious.

Seated on God's throne, the lamb becomes the shepherd who guides the new flock to the fountains of the waters of life (Apoc. 7:16). His lambs listen to his voice in faith, drink the clear waters of the spirit from the fountains of Baptism, and feed on the flesh of the pastor in the Eucharist. During their earthly life, "they are reckoned no better than sheep marked down for the slaughter" (Rom. 8:36), until the final triumph of the lamb. Then, skipping over the hills of eternity, they will sing the new song of the lamb.

V.A.Mc.

11:116,1), claiming that God had always desired to save the human flock: "Therefore, the good Lord sent also the good shepherd."

Representations of shepherds are known from classical antiquity from as early as the beginning of the great age of Greek sculpture in the seventh century B.C. These were votive gifts, symbolic of the worshiper offering his sacrificial animal to the deity. Figures of shepherds formed part of the repertory of bucolic themes in Classic-Hellenistic times. Rome was to

65) CASKET FOR A RELIQUARY OF THE TRUE CROSS; Rome, 817–24; silver, with partial gilding, and niello; height 3⅞″, width 9⅞″, length 11⅝″, thickness of silver 1/16″. *Biblioteca Apostolica Vaticana, Museo Sacro*, Vatican City

This cross-shaped casket once held a richly gemmed gold cross that contained particles of the True Cross of Christ. It was made for Pope Paschal I (817–24), according to the niello inscription surrounding the central scene of the Communion of the Apostles on the lid. The casket and its cross were discovered early in this century with other relics and reliquaries in a cypress-wood chest that Pope Leo III (795–816) had placed in the main altar of the Oratory of San Lorenzo, the *Sancta Sanctorum*, which served as the private chapel of the popes at the *Palazzo Lateranense*, their residence. The earliest reference to the silver casket occurs in the twelfth-century inventory of the oratory written by John the Deacon during the reign of Alexander III (1159–81). The casket is made of thick sheets of silver cut and soldered together and worked in repoussé on the lid and sides with scenes of events from the life of Christ. Christ among the Doctors (Luke 2:46), the Marriage at Cana (John 2:1), Christ's Mission to the Apostles (Matthew 28:16–20), and His appearance to the apostles after His resurrection (John 20:19–29) encircle the lid's central Communion scene. The sides are decorated with a cycle of events that followed Christ's resurrection, including the discovery of the empty tomb by the holy women (Matthew 28:1–10; John 20:1–12), Christ's appearance to the apostles at Emmaus, as well as other appearances to His apostles (Luke 24:36–50; John 20:19–29)—beginning with an unusual scene that may depict Christ conducting Adam from Hades, as related in the Apocryphal Gospels. The emphasis on events after the Crucifixion is appropriate for a reliquary that contained the "life-giving" cross.

M. E. F.

GALLERY SIX

RAPHAEL, TAPESTRY OF THE "SCUOLA NUOVA" (detail)

"I am the Resurrection and the Life. . ." (John 11:25)

66) RAPHAEL; 1483–1520; **TAPESTRY OF THE "SCUOLA NUOVA";** 16th century; made from Raphael drawings by the "Scuola Nuova"; wool and silk; height 197″, width 375⅘″. *The Tapestry Gallery,* Vatican City

This magnificent tapestry of the Risen Christ is one of a series depicting incidents in the life, death, and resurrection of Jesus Christ. It was possibly commissioned by Pope Clement VII or by Pope Leo X, either as a part of the Sistine Chapel series, or as a series subsequently commissioned for special papal occasions. It is a rich cross-section of hues of gold, yellow, brown, red, all blended in a magnificent way to portray that triumphal moment when Jesus Christ broke the bonds of death and sin and rose gloriously from the dead.

From 1515 to 1516, Raphael supplied drawings for a series of tapestries to be hung on solemn occasions along the walls of the Sistine Chapel, under the *Quattrocento* scenes of Christ and Moses. The designs were sent to Brussels in 1517 where they were woven out of silk and wool in the workshops of Peter van Velst. Their execution was flawless. When at Christmas time 1519, the finished tapestries were hung on the walls and exhibited to the people of Rome, they created a sensation. The one representing the Risen Christ is considered one of the most beautiful. The elegance of its lines and the measured harmony of the whole focus on the Risen Christ, and create an impression of awe at this most sublime moment.

Raphael was concerned not only with the beauty of the work of art, but with the world of Christian redemption and that of platonic ideals so common in the Renaissance. Thus there came together during Raphael's life the combination of concern for the human condition in terms of the humanistic circle of Lorenzo di Medici, and the other in terms of the religious teachings of the Dominican, Savonarola. Raphael portrays no opposition between the two, but rather reveals a more artistic and emotional fusion of them both. Christ, emerging triumphant with his banner, having conquered death and sin, stresses the act of redemption as being completed. Raphael chose not to portray pain in the usual medieval way, seeking rather to communicate the perfect beauty of the Risen Christ. In so doing he wed the classical tradition as it was rediscovered in the Renaissance, and the notion of Christian redemption, the ultimate act of transcendent beauty manifested to the world through the body of the Risen Christ.

V.A.Mc.

---

67) MICHELANGELO BUONARROTI, 1475–1564; CHRIST RESURRECTED: 1519–20; marble; height 81″. *Church of Santa Maria sopra Minerva, Rome, Italy*

No collection of Vatican art treasures would be complete without some representation of the most distinguished and famous of the painters and sculptors of the Vatican, Michelangelo. While the frescos of the Sistine Chapel reveal the genius of his painting, still the *Statue of the Risen Christ* reveals his genius as a sculptor—even though it was left incomplete by him. Fortunately, through the special permission of the Dominican Province of Rome and the Department of Fine Arts (*Belle Arti*) of the Italian Government, we have on loan to the New Orleans Vatican Pavilion this magnificent Michelangelo masterpiece. In order to appreciate it in its proper perspective, we need to look briefly at the background from which it comes and the period of his life when he was most productive.

In March, 1505, Michelangelo went to Rome at the request of Pope Julius II (1503–1513). He was summoned to Rome to begin plans for a monumental tomb for the Pope, but before he could begin his preparations for this task he discovered that his patron had even greater plans for him, something even more important, namely, the restoration and remodeling of St. Peter's itself. Michelangelo soon discovered that his patron, Julius II, was a man of great vision and was intent upon accomplishing many projects. Immediately, Julius commissioned him to paint the twelve apostles, and a few ornaments in the ceiling of the Sistine Chapel. Michelangelo was to spend the next five years of his life painting more than three hundred figures on the ceiling of that Chapel—from 1509 to 1515. Between the lunettes and spandrels Michelangelo depicted Christ's spiritual ancestors, the prophets, and the sybils as well—combining Old Testament and classical themes. Each figure seems totally wrapped in a spiritual act of contemplation and ecstasy. Michelangelo's *Paradise* is not a dazzling garden, as one would think. It is, rather, Adam and Eve alone, with only the Tree of Knowledge attracting their attention. In Michelangelo's conception of things, the woman is no longer the guilty party; but both Adam and Eve are guilty to the same extent and are molded together into an indissoluble unity, unable to resist the desire for the knowledge made so attractive by the Tree.

As Michelangelo continues his Creation, the means of representation become more elementary as the events go further back towards the origins of the world. The figure of God creating Eve occupies almost a third of this fresco. In the creation of Adam, God and man appear almost as equals. Adam lies on raised rocks and, lifting himself up slightly, without any show of effort, he stretches out his arm towards God. God arrives, floating in space, his powerful cloak flying about him, accompanied by angels. Michelangelo does not show us the event of man's creation, but the moment in which man receives his soul. Finally, Michelangelo shows God creating earthly matter and light; God with raised arms and spinning with a whirlwind effect creates the primaeval matter to generate the first element.

While completing the ceiling of the Sistine Chapel, in 1513, his patron, Pope Julius II, died. By 1516, Michelangelo was busy working for a new patron, Giovanni di Medici, who was elected as Julius' successor, and took the name of Pope Leo X (1513–1523).

In 1520 and 1521, Michelangelo received a commission for the Medici Chapel to be built in Florence. It was for this chapel that the artist planned groupings of figures dedicated to the theme of the Resurrection. On the entrance wall, the *Madonna as the Lux Aeterna*

was to stand above the tomb of *Magnifico* with the two patron saints of the Medici family, Cosmas and Damian, on either side. Two figures of nude men should have lain at their feet, as personifications of rivers as the sources of life. A representation of Christ's Resurrection had been planned for the lunette crowning the whole of this grouping. Finally, two candelabra at the altar on the opposite wall represent the pelican as the symbol of self-sacrifice, and the phoenix as the symbol of the Resurrection.

In 1519 to 1520 Michelangelo worked on his famous *Statue of the Risen Christ*—a representation of Christ carrying the cross in triumph, having conquered death and sin. By stressing the resurrection event he was not overlooking the great price paid for the act of redemption. He often reflected on the lines from the *Divine Comedy*, "One does not think how much blood it costs," referring to the redemption brought about by the suffering and shedding of Christ's blood. Here, however, in the *Risen Christ* he is concentrating on the sublime moment of the conquest over death and sin. For him, this was best personified in the wedding of beauty with the truth of the cross.

According to Vasari, this Michelangelo statue is "one of the most heroic statues portraying the Risen Christ."

The work, in fact, was brought to Rome in 1521 and finished by the Roman artist, Pierto Urbano and his associate, Federico Frizzi.

V.A.Mc.

MICHELANGELO BUONAROTTI; 1475–1564; **THE SISTINE CHAPEL:** 1509–1515; fresco. Vatican City

The frescos of The Sistine Chapel were created by Michelangelo from 1509 to 1515. They reveal his ge-

nius as a painter. It is in this Chapel that each new Pope is elected.

V.A.Mc.

SAINT PETER AND HIS SUCCESSORS

This list of popes and antipopes is derived from one compiled by A. Mercati in 1947 under the auspices of the Vatican, though some changes have been made on the basis of recent scholarship and the list has been brought up to date. The dates of each pope's reign follow his name; for popes after the end of the Great Schism (1378–1417), family names are given as well. The names of antipopes are enclosed in brackets, while alternative numberings of papal names appear in parentheses.

SAINT PETER (67)
SAINT LINUS (67–76)
SAINT ANACLETUS (CLETUS) (76–88)
SAINT CLEMENT I (88–97)
SAINT EVARISTUS (97–105)
SAINT ALEXANDER I (105–15)
SAINT SIXTUS I (115–25)
SAINT TELESPHORUS (125–36)
SAINT HYGINUS (136–40)
SAINT PIUS I (140–55)
SAINT ANICETUS (155–66)
SAINT SOTER (166–75)
SAINT ELEUTHERIUS (175–89)
SAINT VICTOR I (189–99)
SAINT ZEPHYRINUS (199–217)
SAINT CALLISTUS I (217–22)
[SAINT HIPPOLYTUS (217–35)]
SAINT URBAN I (222–30)
SAINT PONTIANUS (230–35)
SAINT ANTERUS (235–36)
SAINT FABIAN (236–50)
SAINT CORNELIUS (251–53)
[NOVATIAN (251)]
SAINT LUCIUS I (253–54)
SAINT STEPHEN I (254–57)
SAINT SIXTUS II (257–58)
SAINT DIONYSIUS (259–68)
SAINT FELIX I (269–74)
SAINT EUTYCHIAN (275–83)
SAINT GAIUS (CAIUS) (283–96)
SAINT MARCELLINUS (296–304)
SAINT MARCELLUS I (308–9)
SAINT EUSEBIUS (309)
SAINT MILTIADES (311–14)
SAINT SILVESTER I (314–35)
SAINT MARK (336)
SAINT JULIUS I (337–52)
LIBERIUS (352–66)
[FELIX II (355–65)]
SAINT DAMASUS I (366–84)
[URSINUS (366–67)]
SAINT SIRICIUS (384–99)

SAINT ANASTASIUS I (399–401)
SAINT INNOCENT I (401–17)
SAINT ZOSIMUS (417–18)
SAINT BONIFACE I (418–22)
[EULALIUS (418–19)]
SAINT CELESTINE I (422–32)
SAINT SIXTUS III (432–40)
SAINT LEO I (440–61)
SAINT HILARY (461–68)
SAINT SIMPLICIUS (468–83)
SAINT FELIX III (II) (483–92)
SAINT GELASIUS I (492–96)
ANASTASIUS II (496–98)
SAINT SYMMACHUS (498–514)
[LAWRENCE (498; 501–5)]
SAINT HORMISDAS (514–23)
SAINT JOHN I (523–26)
SAINT FELIX IV (III) (526–30)
BONIFACE II (530–32)
[DIOSCORUS (530)]
JOHN II (533–35)
SAINT AGAPITUS I (535–36)
SAINT SILVERIUS (536–37)
VIGILIUS (537–55)
PELAGIUS I (556–61)
JOHN III (561–74)
BENEDICT I (575–79)
PELAGIUS II (579–90)
SAINT GREGORY I (590–604)
SABINIAN (604–6)
BONIFACE III (607)
SAINT BONIFACE IV (608–15)
SAINT DEUSDEDIT I (615–18)
BONIFACE V (619–25)
HONORIUS I (625–38)
SEVERINUS (640)
JOHN IV (640–42)
THEODORE I (642–49)
SAINT MARTIN I (649–55)
SAINT EUGENE I (654–57)
SAINT VITALIAN (657–72)
DEUSDEDIT II (672–76)

DONUS (676–78)
SAINT AGATHO (678–81)
SAINT LEO II (682–83)
SAINT BENEDICT II (684–85)
JOHN V (685–86)
CONON (686–87)
[THEODORE (687)]
[PASCHAL (687)]
SAINT SERGIUS I (687–701)
JOHN VI (701–5)
JOHN VII (705–7)
SISINNIUS (708)
CONSTANTINE (708–15)
SAINT GREGORY II (715–31)
SAINT GREGORY III (731–41)
SAINT ZACHARY (741–52)
STEPHEN (752)
STEPHEN II (III) (752–57)
SAINT PAUL I (757–67)
[CONSTANTINE (767–69)]
[PHILIP (768)]
STEPHEN III (IV) (768–72)
ADRIAN I (772–95)
SAINT LEO III (795–816)
STEPHEN IV (V) (816–17)
SAINT PASCHAL I (817–24)
EUGENE II (824–27)
VALENTINE (827)
GREGORY IV (827–44)
[JOHN (844)]
SERGIUS II (844–47)
SAINT LEO IV (847–55)
BENEDICT III (855–58)
[ANASTASIUS (855)]
SAINT NICHOLAS I (858–67)
ADRIAN II (867–72)
JOHN VIII (872–82)
MARINUS I (882–84)
SAINT ADRIAN III (884–85)
STEPHEN V (VI) (885–91)
FORMOSUS (891–96)
BONIFACE VI (896)
STEPHEN VI (VII) (896–97)
ROMANUS (897)
THEODORE II (897)
JOHN IX (898–900)
BENEDICT IV (900–903)
LEO V (903)
[CHRISTOPHER (903–4)]
SERGIUS III (904–11)
ANASTASIUS III (911–13)
LANDO (913–14)
JOHN X (914–28)
LEO VI (928)
STEPHEN VII (VIII) (928–31)
JOHN XI (931–35)
LEO VII (936–39)
STEPHEN VIII (IX) (939–42)

MARINUS II (942–46)
AGAPETUS II (946–55)
JOHN XII (955–64)
LEO VIII (963–65)
BENEDICT V (964–66)
JOHN XIII (965–72)
BENEDICT VI (973–74)
[BONIFACE VII (974; 984–85)]
BENEDICT VII (974–83)
JOHN XIV (983–84)
JOHN XV (985–96)
GREGORY V (996–99)
[JOHN XVI (997–98)]
SILVESTER II (999–1003)
JOHN XVII (1003)
JOHN XVIII (1004–9)
SERGIUS IV (1009–12)
BENEDICT VIII (1012–24)
[GREGORY (1012)]
JOHN XIX (1024–32)
BENEDICT IX (1032–44)
SILVESTER III (1045)
BENEDICT IX (1045)
GREGORY VI (1045–46)
CLEMENT II (1046–47)
BENEDICT IX (1047–48)
DAMASUS II (1048)
SAINT LEO IX (1049–54)
VICTOR II (1055–57)
STEPHEN IX (X) (1057–58)
[BENEDICT X (1058–59)]
NICHOLAS II (1059–61)
ALEXANDER II (1061–73)
[HONORIUS II (1061–72)]
SAINT GREGORY VII (1073–85)
[CLEMENT III (1080; 1084–1100)]
BLESSED VICTOR III (1086–87)
BLESSED URBAN II (1088–99)
PASCHAL II (1099–1118)
[THEODORIC (1100)]
[ALBERT (1102)]
[SILVESTER IV (1105–11)]
GELASIUS II (1118–19)
[GREGORY VIII (1118–21)]
CALLISTUS II (1119–24)
HONORIUS II (1124–30)
[CELESTINE II (1124)]
INNOCENT II (1130–43)
[ANACLETUS II (1130–38)]
[VICTOR IV (1138)]
CELESTINE II (1143–44)
LUCIUS II (1144–45)
BLESSED EUGENE III (1145–53)
ANASTASIUS IV (1153–54)
ADRIAN IV (1154–59)
ALEXANDER III (1159–81)
[VICTOR IV (1159–64)]
[PASCHAL III (1164–68)]

[CALLISTUS III (1168–78)]
[INNOCENT III (1179–80)]
LUCIUS III (1181–85)
URBAN III (1185–87)
GREGORY VIII (1187)
CLEMENT III (1187–91)
CELESTINE III (1191–98)
INNOCENT III (1198–1216)
HONORIUS III (1216–27)
GREGORY IX (1227–41)
CELESTINE IV (1241)
INNOCENT IV (1243–54)
ALEXANDER IV (1254–61)
URBAN IV (1261–64)
CLEMENT IV (1265–68)
BLESSED GREGORY X (1271; 1272–76)
BLESSED INNOCENT V (1276)
ADRIAN V (1276)
JOHN XXI (1276–77)
NICHOLAS III (1277–80)
MARTIN IV (1281–85)
HONORIUS IV (1285–87)
NICHOLAS IV (1288–92)
SAINT CELESTINE V (1294)
BONIFACE VIII (1294; 1295–1303)
BLESSED BENEDICT XI (1303–4)
CLEMENT V (1305–14)
JOHN XXII (1316–34)
[NICHOLAS V (1328–30)]
BENEDICT XII (1335–42)
CLEMENT VI (1342–52)
INNOCENT VI (1352–62)
BLESSED URBAN V (1362–70)
GREGORY XI (1370; 1371–78)
URBAN VI (1378–89)
BONIFACE IX (1389–1404)
INNOCENT VII (1404–6)
GREGORY XII (1406–15)
[CLEMENT VII (1378–94)]
[BENEDICT XIII (1394–1423)]
[ALEXANDER V (1409–10)]
[JOHN XXIII (1410–15)]
MARTIN V (COLONNA, 1417–31)
EUGENE IV (CONDULMER, 1431–47)
[FELIX V (1439; 1440–49)]
NICHOLAS V (PARENTUCELLI, 1447–55)
CALLISTUS III (BORGIA, 1455–58)
PIUS II (PICCOLOMINI, 1458–64)
PAUL II (BARBO, 1464–71)
SIXTUS IV (DELLA ROVERE, 1471–84)
INNOCENT VIII (CIBO, 1484–92)
ALEXANDER VI (BORGIA, 1492–1503)
PIUS III (TODESCHINI-PICCOLOMINI, 1503)
JULIUS II (DELLA ROVERE, 1503–13)
LEO X (MEDICI, 1513–21)
ADRIAN VI (FLORENSZ, 1522–23)
CLEMENT VII (MEDICI, 1523–34)
PAUL III (FARNESE, 1534–49)

JULIUS III (CIOCCHI DEL MONTE, 1550–5)
MARCELLUS II (CERVINI, 1555)
PAUL IV (CARAFA, 1555–59)
PIUS IV (MEDICI, 1559; 1560–65)
SAINT PIUS V (GHISLIERI, 1566–72)
GREGORY XIII (BONCOMPAGNI, 1572–85)
SIXTUS V (PERETTI, 1585–90)
URBAN VII (CASTAGNA, 1590)
GREGORY XIV (SFONDRATI, 1590–91)
INNOCENT IX (FACCHINETTI, 1591)
CLEMENT VIII (ALDOBRANDINI, 1592–1605)
LEO XI (MEDICI, 1605)
PAUL V (BORGHESE, 1605–21)
GREGORY XV (LUDOVISI, 1621–23)
URBAN VIII (BARBERINI, 1623–44)
INNOCENT X (PAMPHILI, 1644–55)
ALEXANDER VII (CHIGI, 1655–67)
CLEMENT IX (ROSPIGLIOSI, 1667–69)
CLEMENT X (ALTIERI, 1670–76)
BLESSED INNOCENT XI (ODESCALCHI, 1676–89)
ALEXANDER VIII (OTTOBONI, 1689–91)
INNOCENT XII (PIGNATELLI, 1691–1700)
CLEMENT XI (ALBANI, 1700–1721)
INNOCENT XIII (CONTI, 1721–24)
BENEDICT XIII (ORSINI, 1724–30)
CLEMENT XII (CORSINI, 1730–40)
BENEDICT XIV (LAMBERTINI, 1740–58)
CLEMENT XIII (REZZONICO, 1758–69)
CLEMENT XIV (GANGANELLI, 1769–74)
PIUS VI (BRASCHI, 1775–99)
PIUS VII (CHIARAMONTI, 1800–1823)
LEO XII (DELLA GENGA, 1823–29)
PIUS VIII (CASTIGLIONI, 1829–30)
GREGORY XVI (CAPPELLARI, 1831–46)
PIUS IX (MASTAI-FERRETTI, 1846–78)
LEO XIII (PECCI, 1878–1903)
SAINT PIUS X (SARTO, 1903–14)
BENEDICT XV (DELLA CHIESA, 1914–22)
PIUS XI (RATTI, 1922–39)
PIUS XII (PACELLI, 1939–58)
JOHN XXIII (RONCALLI, 1958–63)
PAUL VI (MONTINI, 1963–78)
JOHN PAUL I (LUCIANI, 1978)
JOHN PAUL II (WOJTYLA, 1978–   )

MICHELANGELO BUONAROTTI; 1475–1564; **CEILING OF THE SISTINE CHAPEL;** 1509–1515; fresco. Vatican City

The ceiling of the Sistine Chapel reveals Michelangelo's vision of the significant events of the book of Genesis and the major Prophets of the Old Testament. At the bottom of reproduction Christ is seen seated in the celebrated Judgment fresco.

V.A.Mc.

CONTRIBUTORS TO THE CATALOGUE

(Catalogue entries have been edited to suit the more popular nature of this catalogue.)

G.M.   **GIOVANNI MORELLO**
Curator, Musei Sacro and Profano, Biblioteca Apostolica Vaticana, Vatican City

R.A.F.   **ROSS A. FOX**
Assistant Curator of Early Canadian Art, National Gallery of Canada

T.N.   **TARA NANAVATI**
Curator, Modern History Division, British Columbia Provincial Museum

J.P.   **JOZEF PENKOWSKI**
Reverend, Curator of the Ethnological Collections, Monumenti Musei e Gallerie Pontificie, Vatican City

W.S.   **WILLIAM SIEGMANN**
Curator, African Art Museum of the Society of African Missions

R.B.   **ROGER BAUDIER**
History of the Church in Louisiana

M.E.F.   **MARGARET ENGLISH FRAZER**
Curator, Department of Medieval Art, The Metropolitan Museum of Art, New York

M.F.   **MARIO FERRAZZA**
Vatican Museums

C.L.C.   **CURTIS L. CARTER**
Committee on the Fine Arts, Marquette University

P.R.   **PIERRE ROSENBERG**
Curator of Paintings, Louvre

F.M.   **FABRIZIO MANCINELLI**
Curator of Byzantine, Medieval, and Modern Art, Monumenti Musei e Gallerie Pontificie, Vatican City

M.W.   **MICHAEL WYNNE**
Keeper, National Gallery of Ireland

G.D.   **GEORG DALTROP**
Curator of Classical Antiquities, Monumenti Musei e Gallerie Pontificie, Vatican City

C.G-M.   **CARMEN GOMEZ-MORENO**
Curator, Department of Medieval Art, The Metropolitan Museum of Art, New York

W.D.W.   **WILLIAM D. WIXOM**
Chairman, Department of Medieval Art and The Cloisters, The Metropolitan Museum of Art, New York

O.R.   **OLGA RAGGIO**
Chairman, Department of European Sculpture and Decorative Arts, The Metropolitan Museum of Art, New York

D.MacK.E.   **DAVID MacKINNON EBITZ**
Assistant Professor, Department of the History of Art, University of Maine, Orono

K.R.B.   **KATHARINE REYNOLDS BROWN**
Senior Research Associate, Department of Medieval Art, The Metropolitan Museum of Art, New York

I.DiS.M.   **IVAN DiSTEFANO MANZELLA**
Assistant Professor, University of Rome

D.K.B.   **DOROTHY K. BURNHAM**
National Gallery of Canada

V.A.Mc.   **VERY REVEREND VAL A. McINNES, O.P.**
Director, New Orleans Vatican Pavilion

R.P.   **REGINE PERNOUD**
Curator, Centre Jeanne d'Arc, Musée Historique Orléans

T.F.   **From *The Treasures of France***

CREDITS

PHOTOGRAPHS

THE AFRICAN ART MUSEUM OF THE SOCIETY OF
   AFRICAN MISSIONS
BASILICA OF ST. JOHN LATERAN
BIBLIOTECA APOSTOLICA VATICANA, MUSEO SACRO
MUSÉE CARNAVALET
ÉGLISE COLLÉGIALE ST. BERNARD, ROMANS
DOCUMENTATION PHOTOGRAPHIQUE DE LA
   RÉUNION DES MUSÉES NATIONAUX, PARIS
REVERENDA FABBRICA DI SAN PIETRO
FLORERIA APOSTOLICA
THE CATHEDRAL OF LYONS
MACDONALD-STEWART FOUNDATION
MARQUETTE UNIVERSITY ART MUSEUM
FRANK H. METHE III
THE HENRY MOORE FOUNDATION
THE NATIONAL GALLERY OF CANADA
THE NATIONAL GALLERY OF IRELAND
THE NATIONAL MAP COLLECTION, PUBLIC
   ARCHIVES, CANADA
THE NATIONAL PUBLIC ARCHIVES OF CANADA
NOTRE DAME DE MONTRÉAL
PAIERIE DEPARTMENTALE DU RHONE
PATRIMOINE DE FRANCE
PONTIFICIO MUSEO MISSIONARIO-ETNOLOGICO
PINACOTECA, MUSEO VATICANO
MUSEO PIO CRISTIANO, LAPIDARIO EBRAICO EX
   LATERANENSE
MUSÉE DU QUÉBEC
THE RINGLING MUSEUM
OSSERVATORE ROMANO
LA SANTA IGLESIA CATEDRAL PRIMADA, TOLEDO
ST. MICHEL D'AIGUILLE, LE PUY, HAÛTE-LOIRE
SACRISTY, SISTINE CHAPEL
THE SNITE MUSEUM
STUDIO C. DEFIVES, VENCE
VATICAN MUSEUMS
JEAN VIGNE, ORLÉANS
WHITEHEAD STUDIOS
HOUSTON MUSEUM OF ART

COPYRIGHT © 1984 NEW ORLEANS VATICAN PAVILION
PUBLISHED BY THE NEW ORLEANS VATICAN PAVILION
VERY REVEREND VAL A. MCINNES, O.P., PH.D.,
   PUBLISHER AND EDITOR IN CHIEF, ASSISTED BY
   PROFESSOR SIMONE FISCHER,
   PROFESSOR ANN HALACK,
   VERY REVEREND RICHARD MURPHY, O.P., S.S.D.,
   MR. DONALD F. SCHULTZ
AND MRS. DOROTHY S. RONIGER

DATE DUE

DEMCO 38-296